Let Us Start Here

Let Us Start Here

* * *

*An Introduction
to Basic Readings
in the Life Sciences*

by PAUL GIBBONS ROOFE

The University of Kansas

The World Publishing Company

CLEVELAND AND NEW YORK

Published by The World Publishing Company
2231 West 110th Street, Cleveland, Ohio 44102

Published simultaneously in Canada by
Nelson, Foster & Scott Ltd.

Library of Congress Catalog Card Number: 66–28440

Printed in the United States of America

To the memory of
Raymond Pearl,
who introduced me to the world's
great books in the life sciences

Preface

I have dedicated this volume to the memory of the late Raymond Pearl (1879–1940), who first introduced his suggestions in a magazine article entitled, "The Reading of Graduate Students" (*The Scientific Monthly,* Vol. XXI, pp. 33–44, July, 1925). It was not the privilege of many of us presently in the field of graduate teaching to have known Professor Pearl except through his small volume *To Begin With* and other writings.

My original idea of placing such a book before the young graduate student in the life sciences was to bring out a reprint of Raymond Pearl's *To Begin With* with an introduction or a foreword, recommending it highly as a guide. Pearl's field was vital statistics and biometry, while the present author's interests are primarily morphological and behavioral. Basically, the original *To Begin With* is probably the best recommended selection of books extant for those who plan to work in the life sciences.

I finally decided that a revamping and updating of the original list would more properly serve the purpose of such an enterprise. Three new chapters: "Brain and Behavior," "Man and the Universe," and "The Strategy of Life" have been added; and "Biostatistics" has been replaced by "Mathematics of Biology." A few of the original books have been deleted; in other cases, books have been substituted for articles.

Any selection of books proposed for a group of interested students will be criticized by those who are concerned in matters of giving proper information to the young, and rightly so. The list presented here is designed primarily for those who are concerned with the fundamental problems of the life sciences, especially problems of behavior as they are related to the evolution of the neural mechanisms involved in learning, with special emphasis on man.

Most students of the life sciences will find value in the entire list, for much of the modern trend is behavioral. Lists are prepared not only to conserve time but also primarily to guide the young in spirit through the great number of books available. The student left alone in a modern library without help or guidance is bewildered. Teachers will give recommendations for special subjects, but the serious student who plans to be well-grounded in his basic area soon learns that he needs guidance. When a list is designed with guidance in view, the young reader is less likely to lose his love of learning.

My motives in presenting this selection have their origin in the pleasures which Pearl's original list presented. If these motives in any way have an "uplifter's" quality about them, the author is unaware of it. Consciously, the author's primary aim is one of guidance and not of uplifting.

Sir John Lubbock, in commenting on one's choice of books, quotes Sir John Herschel, the famous British astronomer: "If I were to pray for a taste which should stand me in stead under every variety of circumstances, and be a source of happiness and cheerfulness to me through life, and a shield against its ills, however things might go amiss, and the world frown upon me, it would be the taste for reading. . . ." Give a man this taste, and the means of gratifying it, and you can hardly fail to make a cheerful and happy man.

Paul Gibbons Roofe

January 1, 1967
Lawrence, Kansas

Contents

CHAPTER ONE

Why and wherefore

In presenting *Let Us Start Here*, I would like to think that I have improved the late Professor Pearl's masterpiece of good-humored advice on the essential reading for graduate students in biology, a small book especially designed to dispel pedantry. The chief aim of Raymond Pearl, the author of *To Begin With*, in making his selections for his book was to help the youthful as well as the seasoned scholar guard against or overcome the handicap of taking himself too seriously. Publisher Alfred A. Knopf kindly permitted me, several years ago, to offer mimeographed copies of selected portions of *To Begin With* to the students in the graduate program in anatomy at The University of Kansas. The original had been out of print for a number of years. This successful effort, coupled with the pleasure that I personally enjoyed during my graduate days, has given me the urge to share this type of literature with others. I am cognizant of the time required of the young men and women preparing to offer professional leadership in biology and related fields in selecting stimulating material. Perhaps this updated treatment will be an acceptable source for an exciting beginning. To this aim I shall address myself.

As to the nature of my urge to continue the ancient custom of recommending reading to the young, I can only say that the virus of which Pearl speaks (he actually dubs this a disease, that is, this urge of book-listing) has infected my blood stream, and the only relief is to purge myself by presenting a revamped list, similar to Pearl's original, to those preparing to give professional training in the biological sciences.

I have a different orientation, since my main interest is in neurological foundations of behavior. Nevertheless, I am using most of Pearl's recommendations with my own reactions to them and, here and there, Pearl's remarks when they express a pungent and penetrating analysis of a book or author.*

The suggested books still are designed more for the young, especially those who are looking forward to a career in the areas of the life sciences; however, those who have reached middle age and beyond will still find considerable pleasure in these selections.

The young students of today at the graduate level are overwhelmed as far as their basic training is concerned. A majority of them are subsidized by federal grants or by foundations. Very few are on their own. These subsidies carry stipends that are more than adequate for a single person. Over one-half of the graduate students are married. In many cases the stipend provides additional funds for dependents. In most graduate schools students are required to devote at least one-half of their time to the research project upon which they are working. The project is usually suggested by their supervisors—a project which fits into the long-term program of the major professor. With half-time effort devoted to research, the graduate student is by rule and regulation not permitted to carry more than two-thirds of the academic load. If he is not employed on a research grant, he is given a teaching assignment that carries the same stipulated time requirement. He is held to a program of required reading in a very narrow field, usually one in which information is expanding at such an explosive rate that

* I am also including Pearl's original chapters "Why" and "Wherefore" as Appendix I and Appendix II, respectively. These chapters and other quotations from *To Begin With* by Raymond Pearl are reprinted by permission of the publisher. Copyright 1927 by Alfred A. Knopf, Inc.

even the major professor cannot keep abreast. He is caught in this vortex, and he has difficulty emerging for a breath of fresh air unless he is given a reading list of classics in his field.

The young neophyte is scheduled for his Ph.D. If he is conscious of the nature of this degree, he soon discovers that something is amiss. To the bright young candidate, the degree implies a possession of knowledge far beyond his narrow range of investigation. But he does not have time to delve deeply into the origin and nature of his own specialty, let alone glean from the classics the essence of his own being and his relation to nature. By "nature" here I mean that which is expressed by Santayana as "the sum total of things potentially observable, some observed actually, others interpolated hypothetically." This, of course, includes the society in which he finds himself, with all its attendant demands and irrationalities. How best may he overcome his plight? Certainly the young student has only so much energy to be expended profitably in a given time at a reasonable rate. One solution is to prolong the training period. But in many cases this cannot be accomplished because of financial circumstances. Another solution might be to require the professorial staff to give an intensive course that would include the essence of the contents of the selections here suggested. This is probably impracticable for reasons that are self-evident; namely, many of the staff themselves are not adequately prepared for such an assignment—and even if they were, few would be willing to sacrifice the time for such missionary work.

Another avenue open is a list of books to be handed to the prospective Ph.D. candidate as soon as practicable in his program in the graduate school, explaining to him that in all probability he might not find time for such a suggested luxury. Further explanation to him should be that while very few of the books would be required reading for the degree, others should be read in order that he might realize he is travelling on the path of a truly educated person. These suggestions are only the beginning. Once the student acquires a taste for such reading, his future is assured.

My suggested reading list has been prepared for a wide range of students in the life sciences. Medical students especially are often lacking a general outlook upon life's meaning and importance. If they continue for more specialized training, this lack is even more acute. Psychiatrists should concern themselves with the entire list, for all chapters bear heavily upon their territory. Psychologists will profit immensely from this list. Sociologists will benefit, for the over-all picture is biologically oriented. The suggestions naturally are aimed at those who are interested in any behavioral approach. The biology student will get much from the general list. In fact, all graduate students might easily profit from the entire book.

What of the background and nature of most of our graduate students in the Occidental world to which this book chiefly is addressed? Are they any different from those of former generations? If so, what are the differences? Are they motivated by the same stimuli as in former times? What are the trends in graduate education?

The present generation of graduate students is the result of the crop of babies born to those of the era that saw the close of World War II. Since their birth the population explosion has almost kept up with the information explosion. They were born into a world subjected to technology, a world which may see total destruction of life on earth or one in which eventually the tools of science will continually be used for the advancement and promotion of a better life. This present age presents an outlook far different from that which faced the parents of those now in graduate training. It is not feasible to treat at length the milieu in which the present graduate students find themselves. It must be said that innately they are no different from preceding generations, but they are faced with an entirely different set of circumstances. There is a saying that no man steps into the same stream twice—indeed, no man steps into the same stream once! This is even more true of large groups living in a rapidly changing world. Conflict, which is a normal component of the living process, is probably more intense in the body politic (both individually and collectively) now (1966) than in previous periods. These conflicts produce new thoughts and behavior patterns and are beneficial if they remain below the pathological level. The exterior motivating mechanisms are different not so much in kind as in degree. The inner motivating mechanisms are also of the same order, but their conditioning has been intensified.

With these intense external conflicts in our international life have come numerous "sputniks" that have spurred many changes in our graduate training programs. The most evident change has been a greater emphasis on a sound training at the secondary school and undergraduate levels, which is evident by the greater number of students enrolling in languages and mathematics. Governments are now more fully aware of the need for highly trained personnel and are making opportunities available to qualified young men and women. The selective processes of obtaining good candidates for the higher degrees are becoming more refined and useful. With an ever-increasing enrollment at all levels of education, it is essential that these processes be refined even more.

It might have been possible a generation ago for a person to enter kindergarten and go to his Ph.D. degree without a hitch, coming out of the process, as Pearl says, "Just another sardine packed in a nice can, not much different from his neighbor." There are, no doubt, many such cases even today. However, recent reports concerning graduate training in the bio-sciences in America indicate that only one in five who enter graduate training finishes with a Ph.D. degree. This, in itself, does not rule out that one still might be "just another sardine";

it does, however, indicate that standards are higher and that more careful scrutiny is being given prospective candidates.

The present-day graduate student, it would seem, needs more than ever a basic plan of reading that will give him a wholesome and unified outlook upon the universe in which he finds himself. He certainly will find that human knowledge is splintered into thousands of bits of information in almost the same number of fields. No matter what area of investigation one enters, if he can leave and return to a home base with comfort, he is less likely to suffer from the individual and social neuroses so prevalent in our times. There is no guarantee that this list will prevent those ills. There is this assurance, however: a firm foundation of thought based upon ideas of past generations aids greatly in making life's journey not only more pleasant but also more meaningful.

CHAPTER TWO

Fundamentals

My list and commentary begins with this chapter. Many casual references will be made to books that will not appear on the numbered roll.

1. TITUS LUCRETIUS CARUS: *De rerum natura*

No doubt many critics of this list would start with a title of a more inclusive nature, such as *Greek Thinkers: A History of Ancient Philosophy,* by Theodor Gomperz. This is an excellent idea, but to emphasize the purpose of this list, I have chosen Lucretius. There are two main reasons for selecting Lucretius. First, in Lucretius' own words, "I love to approach the untasted springs and to quaff, I love to cull fresh flowers and gather for my head a distinguished crown from spots where muses have yet veiled the brows of none; first, because I teach of great things and essay to release the mind from the fast bonds of religious scruples." This statement alone would put the book at the head of any list prepared by one who is sensitive to the present world's enthrallment with religious orthodoxy. As it now appears, Communism is a world religion, endowed with all the trimmings of a vigorous young church, including a holy trinity of Marx, Lenin, and its most current saint. Its creeds indicate its future path, which, no doubt, will be quite similar to the old orthodoxy from which it sprung. The West, with its fundamentalist and splintered groups of religious zealots, also needs the prodding of a Lucretius, for science is in its ascendancy here as well as in the East.

7

The second reason for placing Lucretius first is again best expressed in his own words, ". . . I have taught what the nature of the mind is and out of what things it is formed into one quickened being with the body, and how it is disserved and returns unto its first beginnings. . . ." Since my narrowed interest is the neurological foundations of behavior, I could not have chosen a more fitting introduction than Lucretius' great poem to head my list. Both quotations are to be found early in Book IV.

Lucretius ranks along with Socrates in his ability to show the young their own minds and how to use them. Both would probably be forced into exile or executed if living today, because of their genius in exposing dogma and superstition.

Greek Thinkers does not carry the "punch" of *De rerum natura;* it is a book of great importance and should be familiar to all who wish to know their intellectual origins. The first volume was translated by Laurie Magnus and published in 1901 by Charles Scribner's Sons, New York. The other volumes were translated by G. G. Berry and published by the same firm in 1905 and 1912.

There are three excellent translations of Lucretius. They are as follow: H. A. J. Munro's prose work is found in the Bohn's Popular Library, published in London by G. Bell and Sons, Ltd., 1926. This translation will, in many ways, be more appealing than the two others. Munro was a fellow of Trinity, who became a professor at Cambridge. As Pearl states, "But teaching bored him, as it has many another honest man and he resigned his post after two years. His translation of Lucretius is a masterpiece at once faithful to the text in a way that only a great scholar can achieve, and at the same time possesses a great literary charm on its own account."

Another translation is Cyril Bailey's *Lucretius on the Nature of Things,* Oxford, Clarendon Press, 1910.

For those who prefer a metrical English version, *Lucretius: Of the Nature of Things: A Metrical Translation* by William Ellery Leonard, Everyman's Library, New York, E. A. Dutton and Co., is suggested.

2. LUCIUS ANNAEUS SENECA: *Quaestiones naturales*

There were three great exponents of Stoicism: Seneca, Epictetus, and Marcus Aurelius. Their social stations differed greatly, but their outlook and teachings were much the same. Philosophy was the science of this period. In our own day science is a variegated array of narrowed specialties, and very few modern politicians are qualified to mix their science with politics. Seneca did—and the consequences were almost disastrous. However, the ascendancy of modern science in government may prove also to be disastrous.

Seneca offers the best of Roman science at the very beginning of the Christian era, especially in astronomy, geology, and meteorology.

Seneca, like Lucretius, "had a lofty conception of the dignity and moral influence of the study of nature." This pursuit seemed to him "to raise us above the sordid things of life and to withdraw the mind from the body—a dissociation so eminently beneficial to our higher aspirations."

Probably the best translation of Seneca's *Quaestiones naturales* is by John Clarke, entitled *Physical Science in the Time of Nero* (Macmillan & Co., 1910). This edition carries notes of exceptional value by Sir Archibald Geike, from which the above quotation was taken.

3. ARISTOTLE: *Historia animalium*

There are two outstanding translations of this classic treatise on the natural history of animals by Aristotle. One is a French rendition by Armand Gaston Camus, published in Paris, in 1783, which supplies abundant biological notes. The other, and by far the better, is by D'Arcy Wentworth Thompson. It consists of Volume Four of *The Works of Aristotle,* translated into English under the editorship of J. A. Smith and W. D. Rose, Oxford, Clarendon Press, 1910. Thompson's work is studded with annotations related to textual points, but lacks annotations concerning biological matters. All students of animal life should know what Aristotle relates, for our Western scientific culture stems from early Greek thinkers.

4. LAWRENCE JOSEPH HENDERSON: *The Order of Nature; An Essay*

This classic holds considerable philosophical fascination. Without order no science exists, especially biological science. The precarious existence of life is admirably portrayed with a short historical account from the time of Aristotle on. The reader soon appreciates why he has been asked to read the three preceding accounts.

Henderson was more than a biochemist; he was a philosopher as well. His earlier book, *The Fitness of the Environment,* depicts the coming into being of the elements of life and its relation to the cosmos. Much has been written concerning the order of nature. André Lwoff's *Biological Order* (MIT Press, Boston, 1962), advances Henderson's thesis to higher levels. A. I. Oparin's delightful little book *Life: Its Nature, Origin and Development,* Academic Press, New York, 1961, should be mentioned, but for sheer portrayal of the problems involved, Henderson's treatment will stand above them all. The reader will, no doubt, be familiar with much of the current work of such men as Fox, Miller, Abelson, and above all, the Nobel prize laureate, Harold Urey, who have contributed much to the nature of life's origin. The enigma of adaptability is, after all, a chemical and physical problem uncomplicated by the riddle of life. *The Order of Nature* was first published by the Harvard Press, Cambridge, 1917. There was a second impression in 1925.

5. LUCIAN OF SAMOSATA: *Vitarum auctio* and *Piscator*

I have now come to a point in my list where one should take stock of the heavy and heady literary diet presented so far. How does it meet the realities faced by the most ridiculous of all animals, Homo sapiens? Lucian, the first great satirist, should be consulted to relieve any tension that may have arisen through the study of nature. Lucian was not a great intellect, but as a thinker he was consistently honest—most of the time. He had an undeviating rationalism coupled with hardheaded skepticism that was simple and clear-cut. Pearl remarks that he was the first truly great human biologist who heads the list of such as Rabelais, Voltaire, Swift, Thomas Love Peacock, Anatole France, George Bernard Shaw, and H. L. Mencken; many of whom were greatly influenced by him.

There are two English translations of Lucian, both of which contain these dialogues. The first is *The Works of Lucian,* by H. W. Fowler and F. G. Fowler, 4 vols., Oxford, Clarendon Press, 1905. The second is by Lionel Casson, Professor of Classics at New York University, which carries the title *Selected Satires of Lucian,* published by Doubleday & Co., Inc., Garden City, New York, 1962, as an Anchor Books paperback edition. The latter does not carry some of the lectures that Lucian gave on his tours of the Provinces, or those presented during his government professorships in Gaul, nor is it as expurgated as the first. There is a French edition translated by Belin de Ballu, edited by Louis Humbert and published by Garnier Frères, Paris, 1896, 2 vols. This one is much less expurgated than either of the others.

For those who wish to be further enlightened by what satire can offer, I recommend Gilbert Highet's *Anatomy of Satire,* Princeton University Press, 1962.

6. ALFRED NORTH WHITEHEAD: *Science and the Modern World* (Lowell Lectures, 1925)

The end of the final paragraph of this influential book is as follows:

> The moral of the tale is the power of reason, its decisive influence on the life of humanity. The great conquerors from Alexander to Caesar, from Caesar to Napoleon, influenced profoundly the lives of subsequent generations. But the total effect of this influence shrinks to insignificance, if compared to the entire transformation of human habits and human mentality produced by the long line of men of thought from Thales to the present day, men individually powerless, but ultimately rulers of the world.

This was written shortly after Whitehead became professor of philosophy at Harvard University, a time in which he began a new career from that of a mathematical logician to one of a metaphysician. Since I take the stand with Herrick (see No. 74) that our science is one in which metaphysics has very little to contribute to the understanding of nature—including human nature—I cannot wholeheartedly agree with Whitehead. If I agreed with him, many other recommended books would not be on our list. However, *Science and the Modern World* made a profound impact upon the intellectual atmosphere in the latter half of the third decade of our century. It stated the case for modern science, perhaps not in the clearest terms, but it summarized what was already "in the air." It still remains an item of considerable importance for our young, budding biologist, for it attempts to unify all nature into an organic whole. In fact, Whitehead treats all things as organisms. Returning to the idea of what was in the air in the twenties, one is reminded of General Jan Christian Smuts's book *Holism and Evolution,* which I include in Chapter 6. *Science and the Modern World* was published in New York by Macmillan in 1925.

7. GEORGE HENRY LEWES: *A Biographical History of Philosophy from Its Origins in Greece Down to the Present Day*

In 1857, D. Appleton & Company, New York, published the first American edition of Lewes' *Biographical History of Philosophy.* Lewes says, "This new edition may almost be considered as a new work. So many are the additions and so extensive the alterations. Seven new names have been added to the list of philosophers—Abelard, Algazzali, Giordano Bruno, Hartley, Darwin, Cabanis, and Gall."

Sir John Lubbock included it in his *Best Hundred Books,* published by George Rutledge & Sons, Ltd., London. Editions from any source are hard to find. It is, because of the "rare quality of philosophical insight" of the author, an outstanding history of philosophy.

As Pearl remarks, "Persons who find philosophy hard or dull reading have never tried Lewes." This particular biographical approach is truly an exciting journey over the paths of philosophy.

*   *   *

Up to this point we have concerned ourselves with what great thinkers of the past have had to say about nature. This has been breath-taking in its scope and depth of penetration. We must admit again with Lucretius and Seneca that such studies and contemplation free one from the sordid workaday world. They ennoble and quicken the mind. They aid in estab-

13

lishing a workable understanding with nature. It is hoped that these studies are only the beginning of a fruitful and pleasant experience in reading the great classics.

* * *

8. FRANCIS BACON: *On the Dignity and Advancement of Learning* and *Novum organum; or True Suggestion for the Interpretation of Nature*

No other man writing before the 18th century had as great a prophetic insight into the nature of science and its potentialities as Francis Bacon. He "saw through time" to use a phrase of Loren Eiseley, the poetical anthropologist (No. 73). Bacon said, "A true scientist should be a man of compassion and understanding." He further warned that knowledge without charity could bite with the deadliness of a serpent's venom.

Bacon was loved by Ben Jonson, but arrogantly sneered at by William Harvey, who remarked, "He writes his science like a Lord Chancellor." His King, James the First, remarked cynically that—to quote Eiseley again—"his work was like the peace of God that passes all understanding."

All students of science should be familiar with the Baconian scientific method and his ideas concerning its implications. Bacon, without a doubt, is truly the father of modern science.

There are many excellent biographies of Bacon. To become acquainted with Bacon, especially in an extremely critical and sympathetic way, Catherine Drinker Bowen's *Francis Bacon, The Temper of a Man* (Boston: Little, Brown; 1963), offers a wholesome portrait of one who suffered disgrace yet was a true nobleman. One should, by all means, read Henry Thomas Buckle's account of Bacon's life and character which was published by Longmans, Green & Co., 1885, under the title of *The Miscellaneous and Posthumous Works of Henry Thomas Buckle* (a new and abridged edition) edited by Grant

14

Allen. The edition I like best of *The Advancement of Learning* and *Novum organum* was published in The World's Great Classics by The Colonial Press Inc., New York, 1900.

9. RENÉ DESCARTES: *Discourse de la méthode pour bien conduire sa raison et chercher la vérité dans les sciences*

Many editions of this book in many languages have appeared. The one that is suggested is entitled *The Method, Meditations and Philosophy of Descartes,* translated from the original texts with a new introductory essay, historical and critical by John Veitch, with a special introduction by Frank Sewall. It was published in 1901 by Tudor Publishing Co., New York.

There are two other English translations that should be mentioned: *The Philosophical Works of Descartes* by Elizabeth Haldane and C. R. T. Ross, published in 1911 by the Cambridge University Press; and Miss Haldane's *Descartes: His Life and Times,* issued by John Murray of London in 1905.

10. WILLIAM WHEWELL: *The History of the Inductive Sciences*

There are several histories of science. The one that stands out most vividly, portraying a comprehensive view with discernment, is the *History of the Inductive Sciences* by William Whewell, D.D., Master of Trinity College, Cambridge. There have been many editions of this famous book, the original having been published in London by John Parker in 1857. Any one edition is as good as another.

11. GUSTAVE FLAUBERT: *Bouvard et Pecuchet*

Many beginning students of science may feel that because a man dedicates his life to science, he possesses some degree of rationality not found among laymen. This illusion is soon dispelled. Probably the scientist is possessed of an overdose of curiosity not commonly found in the nonscientists. Certainly this, coupled with a vivid imagination, is essential to a successful career in science. This list abounds with recommendations and references to the great satirists of the Western world. Flaubert, through the lives and words of Bouvard and Pecuchet, brings home to scientists a satire that truly hurts. It should be read by all who seriously plan a life devoted to the pursuit of science. Once the reader has tasted the works of great authors, his appetite will be whetted for more. Flaubert is no exception to this; his *Madame Bovary* and *Salammbô* will long be remembered.

Any of the complete works of Flaubert will have this satirical masterpiece. The one recommended is published by the St. Dunstan Society, Akron, Ohio, 1904.

12. KARL PEARSON: *The Grammar of Science*

Bacon has set the stage for modern science, and Karl Pearson has written the grammar by which it should be described. He was more than a practicing scientist. He was psychologist, philosopher, and humanist. A mathematician of considerable stature, he presents his material in a clear, terse fashion. Raymond Pearl remarks that no other book has given him such an intellectual outlook. There have been four issues of this. In 1892 Walter Scott of London published it in the Contemporary Science Series. Adam and Charles Black of London published three editions: the first and probably the best was in 1900; the last in 1911. There is an excellent edition in the Everyman's Library, J. M. Dent & Sons, Ltd., London, 1937, one year after Pearson died.

13. FERDINAND CANNING SCOTT SCHILLER: *Formal Logic, a Scientific and Social Problem*

This subject is the most "tricky" of all the books on the list. No one knows this better than Schiller himself, who performs an admirable task in showing us how inconsistent formal logicians can be. The book is written in a most urbane manner by a great humanist, whose psychology is not only natural, but also pungent and enlightening.

The author relates his reason for continuing the subject of formal logic:

> Thus Formal Logic has survived, in spite, and largely by reason, of its falsity, and so long as it survives in examination papers its technicalities have to be taught. But they should be taught in a critical spirit, and with a minimum of pedantry and reverence for forms. It is such a critical textbook, for the use of the more progressive teachers in a most unprogressive subject, that I have tried to produce, hoping that it may be provisional and succeed in superseding the need for its own existence.

Formal Logic was published by The Macmillan Co., New York, in a first edition in 1912 and again with a second in 1931.

*　　*　　*

At this juncture it is wise to pause, take note again of the foundation laid by the previous reading. We can now suggest a little lighter perspective which, in many ways, permits a pleasant, sweeping picture on the broad canvas of what has actually gone before.

*　　*　　*

14. HENRY THOMAS BUCKLE: *History of Civilization in England*

Academic historians may not agree with this selection. It is placed here for one main reason: it gives in one panoramic scene a view of man's attempts at civilization in the modern Western world. Buckle was a prodigious scholar. It is reported that he read and mastered the contents of over 21,000 books, written in 19 languages, on every conceivable subject. He averaged three volumes daily. One early review stated that a reader would be truly an educated man if he mastered Buckle's *History of Civilization in England*. Pearl remarks that "not many books as interesting have ever been written."

There is an American edition published in 1885 by D. Appleton & Co., of New York.

Buckle was truly a remarkable man! Those who wish further notes concerning his life might consult *The Life and Writings of Henry Thomas Buckle* by Alfred Henry Huth, published by D. Appleton & Co., New York, 1880.

15. JOHN THEODORE MERZ: *A History of European Thought in the Nineteenth Century*

To obtain a clearer understanding of the nature of history, one should not miss this great book. The introduction alone is worth its inclusion, for the author argues soundly for the place and power of thought in the history of man with all its intrigues, passions, and irrationalities. It was published in four volumes by William Blackwood & Sons, in Edinburgh and London, in 1903.

16. ARTHUR TILLEY: *François Rabelais*

Few people have heard of Rabelais—much less have they understood his place in the world of letters. Tilley's account is superb and is placed at this point to give the reader a firmer understanding of Rabelais' place in the history of French literature and his true role as a human biologist, especially at the satirical level. The book was published in 1907, by Lippincott in Philadelphia, as part of a series of French Men of Letters, edited by Alexander Jessup.

17. FRANÇOIS RABELAIS: *Five Books of the Lives, Heroic Deeds and Sayings of Gargantua and His Sonne Pantagruel*

Modern man needs another Rabelais on a cosmic scale. Rabelais' characters, "Gargantuan" in all respects, are great, but not quite big enough to jar Homo sapiens into his senses before he blows himself off this little particle of dust floating in the immense reaches of the cosmos. Once the reader becomes enthralled with the heroic deeds and sayings of the good Pantagruel, he will remain forever a member of that small, select band of Pantagruelists.

There are many editions of this famous classic. The original was in Old French. Probably the best translation is by W. F. Smith; it appeared in London in 1893, published for subscribers only, by Alexander P. Watt under the title of *Rabelais: The Five Books and Minor Writings with Letters and Documents, Illustrating His Life.* A second edition was published in 1934 by the Cambridge University Press. Attention should be called to the Jacques Le Clerq translation in the Modern Library Series (New York: Random House, 1944). The Viking Press, New York, 1962, published a paperback entitled *The Portable Rabelais.*

CHAPTER THREE

Living

The business of living is the most important and difficult task that nature has bestowed upon man. One branch of learning which deals with living is called ethics. Much has been written on the subject since Aristotle wrote his Nicomachean Ethics. *No treatise dealing directly with ethics is included here. Living has to be experienced. That which follows in this chapter touches only indirectly the basic problems. I like to think that those who make science their goal will eventually find that their philosophy, as well as their psychology, will remain dynamic and naturalistic, a philosophy not of Being but of Becoming, not of Life but of Living.*

None of my listings attempt to preach. Where the authors give advice, it is with sly humor, in good taste, and completely lacks the uplifter's nauseating drivel. From the lives depicted, the reader will gather vicariously much that will be incorporated into his unique way of getting on in the world. About the suggestions I have no doubts. As my title indicates, the list is only a beginning. It is designed to give insight and good-humored counsel. As life has brought some degree of cheerfulness to those herein mentioned, so too can I expect that reading them will bring some happiness.

18. BALTASAR GRACIÁN Y MORALES: *The Art of Worldly Wisdom*

I begin my list concerning the conduct of life with one of the world's best epigrammatists, the urbane Jesuit college president, Baltasar Gracián. Pearl called him "the transcendent—nay the truly miraculous—university president." He is the most fitting to head our list related to the business of living. Only one fault can I find with Gracián in his *Art of Worldly Wisdom*: he said nothing of the importance of the gracious influence of woman as inspirer and counselor in the battle of life. Mention should be made of two other significant men who possessed the art of the maxim and epigram: Jean Rostand in *The Substance of Man,* translated by Irma Brandeis and published in 1962, New York, by Doubleday & Co., and Rochefoucauld through his *Reflections and Moral Maxims,* published by David McKay Co., Philadelphia. Neither of these can equal Gracián, possibly because Gracián was a Jesuit and also a Spaniard—a combination which gives to his maxims a worldly note and a proverbial ring. Gracián is worldly-wise, which makes his book a contrast of hightonedness and shrewdness.

Gracián wrote many books, but only one stands out with any importance—*Oráculo manual y arte de prudencia* (*The Art of Worldly Wisdom*). Schopenhauer used it as a basis for his *Parerga und Paralipomena* and especially *Aphorismen zur Lebensweisheit.* Each maxim is in no sense a shining jewel placed in a brilliant setting. Many are set in a duller background, but in the main they carry a terseness that demands attention. The great moral of the book is to be prudent. If this is so, does it seem worthwhile to try to succeed and is life really worth living? Gracián says that it is in a much more pleasant and acceptable manner than Schopenhauer. He refers many times to luck, how one may trust his luck, follow his luck, etc.

As Pearl remarks about him, "The genial old rascal missed no bets. Also, no other book ever written is so insidiously subversive of all the stated principles of Christian ethics, while maintaining itself on the highest moral planes throughout." There are many editions in many languages, but the one recommended is an exceptionally well-translated and well-edited rendition in English by Joseph Jacobs, with a remarkable biographical introduction. It was published by The Macmillan Company under the above title in 1936 in the Golden Treasury Series.

19. Honoré de Balzac: *Physiologie du Marriage*

Balzac's somewhat cynical treatise on marriage is not what the title implies. It is placed in the list at this point, for it is delightful reading on a subject which treats of the most difficult of all life's problems, namely, man's attempt at regulating his adaptation to the patterns of modern marriage. There are several editions of this book. Mention is made of two, one by the Casanova Society and the other privately printed in London in 1904.

20. Henry Louis Mencken: *In Defense of Women*

As we have pointed out, Mencken is among the élite of human biologists. He had much to say about women. When one reads this book, it is soon apparent that *In Defense of Women* is not a defense of women. We read, "The average woman, until art comes to her aid, is ungraceful, mis-shapen, badly calved and crudely articulated, even for a woman. If she has a good torso, she is almost sure to be bowlegged. If she has good legs, she is almost sure to have bad teeth. If she has good teeth, she is almost sure to have scrawny hands, or muddy eyes, or hair like oakum, or no chin." The book abounds with insult after insult, and many women on reading it hurled it across the room. Actually, this book is not, as it appears, a sarcastic attack on women. On the contrary, it is an attack on men. "The implicit syllogism of the work is: Women are despicable; but women are better than men; therefore, men are even more despicable than women." Mencken goes on to say, "Regardless of woman's shortcomings, she is far superior to man." This is truly Mencken at his best.

The reader will receive from Mencken an insight into American life of the second and third decade of the twentieth century that no other writer has approached. One should read Mencken further. His other writings are as spicy and carry considerable insight, regardless of their subject.

This classic treatise is only one of many essays on human biology by Mencken. It was originally published by Alfred A. Knopf, Inc., New York, in 1922, but has been recently reissued, in paperback, by Time, Inc., New York, 1963. Quoted by permission of Alfred A. Knopf, Inc.

21. II. W. FOWLER: *A Dictionary of Modern English Usage*

No practicing scientist in the biological field can survive the modern academic contest unless he does some writing, truly good writing. To do this, he should be familiar with his native tongue. Very few books will bring to him as much down to earth, good advice on the use of words as this little dictionary. It contains sly humor and good technical advice on our very difficult language.

The book was published by the Clarendon Press at Oxford, 1927. In 1958, a paperback was issued by the New American Library of World Literature as a Signet Book; in 1965, a second edition was published.

22. HENRY MORLEY: *Palissy the Potter. The Life of Bernard Palissy, of Saintes, His Labours and Discoveries in Art and Science with an Outline of His Philosophical Doctrines and a Translation of Illustrative Selections from His Works*

The trials and tribulations of Bernard Palissy were numerous and painful. He founded the first Academy of Science in Paris.

He was a self-educated man. France was in turbulent times three centuries ago, but Palissy was a man obscurely great among the prominently little, "voyaging through strange seas of thought, alone." He travelled about France making beautiful pottery and studying nature by direct observation. There are few men of science who have given us as great an example of courage, fortitude, and genius as Palissy. Pearl remarks that he was "one of the greatest human beings that ever lived." He was at all times creating new things and discovering new truths. All young scientists and artists can get inspiration from Palissy, a truly great personality.

There are American and British editions of these two volumes on Palissy. The American edition was published in 1853 by Ticknor, Reed, & Fields, Boston. The previous year Chapman and Hall of London had brought out the British edition.

23. HUGH MILLER: *My Schools and School Masters; or, The Story of My Education*

Under our present system of grants and grants-in-aid from federal agencies and private sources, the young student of today is totally oblivious to the difficulties encountered by former generations of students in their struggle for training in higher educational centers. For a present-day student to read the autobiography of Hugh Miller, it "must seem like a prehistoric fairy tale," to quote Pearl. Hugh Miller's name is less known than those of many other scientists, but few men have left a more profound impression on the moral fiber of our profession.

Another name, Henry Adams, comes to mind when one considers the education and schooling of apprentices in graduate training. *The Education of Henry Adams* should be placed in our chapter "Man and the Universe," for it is clearly an attempt to put the individual in the scheme of things, especially that which has to do with the perspectives of man's struggle, historically speaking. This book contains as exciting a theory of history as one will find. Along with his "Mont Saint-Michel et Chartres," *The Education of Henry Adams* will give the reader a new insight into the power struggle among peoples of the earth. The 1918 edition appeared in Boston & New York, published by Houghton Mifflin Co., carrying an editor's preface by Henry Cabot Lodge.

Hugh Miller's autobiography is found in many editions. Attention is called to two: the 13th, dated in Edinburgh, published by W. P. Nimmo, 1869; and an American one, issued by Gould and Lincoln, Boston, 1854.

24. Francis Darwin: *The Life and Letters of Charles Darwin Including an Autobiographical Chapter*

Francis Darwin's devotion to the editing of the letters and to the biography of his father is almost equal to the devotion of Charles Darwin to the ideals of science. Both should be carefully noted by all graduate students of biology. Few men have influenced the world's thinking as has Charles Darwin.

The biography is as unbiased as a son could make it. *More Letters of Charles Darwin,* in two volumes, was edited later (1903) by his son Francis and A. C. Seward and published by the same publisher of the original (1887), John Murray of London. Henrietta Litchfield edited a two-volume edition, *Emma Darwin: A Century of Family Letters 1792–1896,* published in 1904 by the Cambridge University Press. We have elsewhere (No. 73) called attention to Eiseley's *Darwin's Century.*

25. Henry Festing Jones: *Samuel Butler: Author of Erewhon (1835–1902) A Memoir*

All Erewhonians will agree that few men of Butler's stature have contributed as much to the literary, artistic, and scientific heritage of the West as Butler. Butler's quarrels with Darwin would be reason alone for the inclusion of this extremely salient biography in the list. Butler was a unique personage, worthy of considerable study. No doubt the reading of the biography will cause the student to delve into Butler's works, which were edited by Henry Festing Jones and A. T. Bartholomew in twenty volumes under the title of *The Shrewsbury Edition of the Works of Samuel Butler,* published by E. P. Dutton & Company of New York in 1926.

Jones's *Memoir* was published in London by Macmillan in 1920, in two volumes.

26. FRANCIS GALTON: *Memories of My Life*

Darwin's cousin, Francis Galton, inherited his interest in nature through a well-ordered genetic and environmental background. His studies on the inheritance of genius bear out his own lineage. The lives of Darwin and Galton should inspire young biologists. These methods of study, habits, and thought processes should be carefully looked into, for they give insight into the ways of scientists, especially biologists.

This remarkable autobiography was published (third edition) by Methuen and Company, London, in 1908.

27. RENÉ VALLERY-RADOT: *The Life of Pasteur*

Modern microbiology and biochemistry are contributing mightily to the basic problems of biology. Pasteur began this great upsurge in the study of the basic life sciences. This outstanding biographical classic was issued by Doubleday, Page & Co., Garden City, New York, in 1919.

28. ANATOLE FRANCE: *Monsieur Bergeret à Paris*

Probably no other great writer has so vividly and poignantly depicted the life of a college professor as Anatole France in this charming book. No one who plans to teach in universities and colleges should miss reading about the fortunes of Monsieur Bergeret. The reader by now has learned that the best way to depict the lives of men is by satire. This book is no exception. Once again the introduction to a great artist whets the appetite for more. Most of Anatole France's works will bring the reader considerable pleasure. There are many editions of France's works, both in French and in English.

29. WILLIAM MORTON WHEELER: *Essays in Philosophical Biology, Selected by Professor G. H. Parker*

It was said of Wheeler that he could have conversed as easily with Aristotle in classical Greek as in his own native language. Certainly he handled many modern languages with facility. His writings will long live as examples of elegant style, for he was very sensitive to the workings of language. As one of America's great biologists, he was able to wield considerable influence in molding the methods of the teaching of biology. His satirical essay "The Dry-Rot of Our Academic Biology" is the clearest expression of this. Probably no other single essay depicts the whole realm of evolution (both inorganic and organic) as does his "Emergent Evolution."

His philosophical writings will long remain classics in their field. No one who professes to be a biologist should neglect these, for they will not only bring insight but also give delight.

These essays were published at the Harvard University Press, Cambridge, in 1939.

30. FRANÇOIS MARIE AROUET DE VOLTAIRE: *Micromégas*

Pearl asked the reader to reread this classic frequently as protection against "becoming seriously important—or importantly serious." In another place we have offered Shapley's *Of Stars and Men* (No. 70) for another purpose. This work will permit no one to take himself too seriously either.

As a poet, historian, and philosopher, Voltaire has few superiors; as a satirical romanticist, he has not even an equal. His *Eastern Romances or Tales* are in the style of the *Arabian Nights* but with far more philosophical and moral implications.

Reading *Micromégas* will entice one to read more of Voltaire. Voltaire is listed here, as in Pearl, as one of the world's truly outstanding human biologists. All of Voltaire's "slightly subversive romances" should be read by all stalwart biologists, who will remain unfulfilled if they do not. There is a well-printed volume entitled *Romans choisis de Voltaire,* which is part of a series entitled *Tous les Chef-d'oeuvres de la Littérature Française,* published in Paris by La Renaissance du Livre (73 Boulevard Saint Michel).

There are many American editions. Attention is called to one: *The Best Known Works of Voltaire, the Complete Romances, Including Candide, The Philosophy of History, The Ignorant Philosopher, Dialogues and Philosophic Criticisms.* This is published by the Blue Ribbon Books, New York, 1927.

31. JAMES BRANCH CABELL: *Straws and Prayer-books. Dizain des Diversions*

The young scientist is surely concerned as to the nature of his "trade," in that he will be anxious to understand the working of his mind. To this end a look into the mind of an artist will immediately convince him that his own creativity is quite similar. Both have a universal base from which to operate. The difference is the media through which expression manifests itself. See Herrick (No. 74) for a more thorough treatment of the mind.

Cabell does a superb job in depicting the workings of the mind of a literary artist. His book was published by McBride, New York, 1924.

32. WILLIAM GRAHAM SUMNER: *Folkways*

Folkways offers an excellent insight into human behavior—which is one of the chief aims of *Let Us Start Here*. Like all true science, it gives no advice; it exposes human behavior in its "complete nudity and objectivity." Our world is rent with neurotic tendencies, with the thermonuclear bombs hanging over each man, woman, and child. It is possible and even probable that man might yet learn how he got this way and take steps to correct his errors. *Folkways* was preliminary to a more exhaustive study and was published by Ginn & Company, Boston. The larger treatise, *The Science of Society,* was later completed, after Sumner's death, by Albert Galloway Keller and Maurice Rea Davie. It was published by the Yale University Press, New Haven, 1927. *Folkways* now appears in paperback, printed by The New American Library of World Literature, New York, 1960, as one in their Mentor Library series.

I also call the reader's attention to another great masterpiece of sociology, *A Treatise on General Sociology* by Vilfredo Pareto. As Pearl remarks:

Nearly everyone has in him some uplifting tendencies which now and again get the upperhand. Pareto is a wonderful help in such cases. Surely few, if any, more completely unemotional and realistic surveys of human nature and human behavior than his treatise on sociology have ever been written. Furthermore, it pioneers towards a sociology which a physicist would recognize and esteem as a science.

33. Lewis S. Feuer: *The Scientific Intellectual. The Psychological and Sociological Origins of Modern Science*

All scientists and prospective scientists should read this book. It is in no way a history of science; far from it. It does present the nature of science and how its votaries became a part of that select band of inquisitive seekers of nature's secrets. The analyses of various cultures plainly show that it is the utilitarian hedonist who has paved the way for scientific enlightenment, and not the esthetic Puritan. The book was published by Basic Books, Inc., of New York and London, in 1963.

CHAPTER FOUR

Biology

It is not the purpose in this chapter to list all or even the great works in the science of biology. We can only suggest those which we think are adapted for our purpose and will whet the interest of those who will follow some phase of life sciences as a profession or goal. We consider these only a prelude, a sort of appetizer to the main dish, which is filled with excitement. When one ponders the nature of things, it is soon discovered that the brain of man is the most tantalizing and complicated structure known. In order to lay a firm foundation from which to view man and his brain-mind complex, the original suggested readings of Pearl seem most appropriate. The brain evolved and functions with the rest of man's anatomical structures. For a firm grasp of this evolutionary history, this list furnishes much that is necessary for a clearer understanding of the coming into being of this natural marvel, the human brain, its capacities and functions.

34. CLAUDIUS GALENUS: *On the Natural Faculties*

Modern medicine rests heavily upon the basic sciences of anatomy, biochemistry, and physiology. Galen was the prime mover of what was known in these fields (other than biochemistry) at the beginning of the Christian era. Few have heard of Galen and still fewer have read him. Galen should be read in order to grasp a more comprehensive understanding of man's struggle with his environment. The most accessible edition of this noted work is found in the Loeb Classical Library with a translation by Arthur John Brock.

35. SIR MICHAEL FOSTER: *Lectures on the History of Physiology During the Sixteenth, Seventeenth and Eighteenth Centuries*

It is fitting that this history of physiology should start with Vesalius. It has been said that the work of Andreas Vesalius of Brussels constitutes one of the greatest treasures of Western Civilization and Culture. All students of biology should have a deep appreciation for the history of physiology. While this small treatise in no way pretends to be complete, it does give considerable insight into the lives of the men who contributed much to the information found in modern physiology and biochemistry.

The content comes from lectures delivered at the Cooper Medical College in San Francisco in the fall of 1900. The first edition appeared in 1901; a reprint was made in 1924 by the Cambridge University Press.

36. WILLIAM HARVEY: *Exercitatio anatomica de motu cordis et sanguinis in animalibus*

No student who professes to understand animal biology should be ignorant of one of the great discoveries of medicine: a clear view of the circulation of the blood. The great Vesalius missed this opportunity because of the Galenic tradition.

There are many editions of this famous classic. The most usable and delightful is a translation with annotations by Chauncey Leake, published by Charles Thomas, Springfield, 1928 (first edition).

37. ROBERT HOOKE: *Micrographia: Or Some Physiological Descriptions of Minute Bodies Made by Magnifying Glasses with Observations and Inquiries Thereupon*

Since the advent of the electron microscope, light microscopy has, to some extent, taken a back seat in modern investigation. However, no matter how penetrating our probes into the infinitesimal may become, we should at least familiarize ourselves with one of the classics in microscopy. Microscopes are to biology what telescopes are to astronomy.

Micrographia is delightful reading. It will introduce the reader to a new historical perspective in microscopic technology which began with Leeuwenhoek and Malpighi. The book was first published in 1665 by the Royal Society. There is now available an admirable reproduction in paperback by the Dover Press, New York, 1961. This facsimile is from the first edition with the index taken from the 1745 and 1780 editions. This 1961 edition contains a preface and a supplementary index by R. T. Gunther.

38. RENÉ ANTOINE FERCHAULT DE RÉAUMUR: *Natural History of Ants. Translated, with an Introduction and Notes, by William Morton Wheeler*

Professor Wheeler's translation and introduction to the *Natural History of Ants* places this truly great classic in its proper light. The ants, termites, and other social insects are at the top of the social ladder among the invertebrates, as the primates are among the vertebrates. To understand primate behavior in its broader biological sense, an insight into what happened to the insects when their brains became smaller, forcing them to a more social life, might be of some help. On the other hand, the enlargement and specialization of the primate brain has affected social behavior among the primates. The book carries the original French text and was published in New York by Alfred A. Knopf, 1926.

39. CHARLES BONNET: *Considérations sur les corps organisés*

Two books on the development of living things are a "must" for all biology scholars, this one and the next in the list. Bonnet was the chief protagonist of the preformationists as opposed to the epigenesists. These two schools have played an important role in the development not only of embryology, but also in biological thinking in general.

There is a fine definitive edition of the collected works of Bonnet (*Oeuvres d'histoire naturelle et de philosophie de Charles Bonnet;* Neuchapel, 1779), of which this is Tome III.

40. CASPER FRIEDRICH WOLFF: *Theoria generationis*

The controversy between preformation and epigenesis has had a long history. Aristotle began the epigenetic approach, which states that living organisms differentiate by an orderly process out of a homogeneous living substrate. Preformation holds that development is merely the unfolding of what is originally present either in the egg or sperm. Pearl likens these two approaches to development to the physicist's concepts of light, the wave theory versus the quantum theory. All students of the life sciences will profit much if they become familiar with these two fundamental concepts of development. There is an excellent German translation by Paul Samassa, published as Nos. 84 and 85 of *Ostwald's Klassiker der exakten Wissenschaften*, Engelmann.

34

41. Sir Charles Bell: *The Hand: Its Mechanism and Vital Endowments as Evincing Design*

Natural theology had its heyday in England at the end of the 18th century and the first half of the 19th century. The Right Honourable and Reverend Francis Henry, Earl of Bridgewater, died in February, 1829. In his will he directed his trustees to work through the President of the Royal Society of London to write, print, and publish one thousand copies of a work, *On the Power, Wisdom and Goodness of God, as manifested in the creation; illustrating such work by all reasonable arguments as for instance the variety and formation of God's creatures in the animal, vegetable, and mineral kingdoms; the effect of digestion, and thereby of conversion; the construction of the hand of man, and an infinite variety of other arguments; as also by discoveries ancient and modern, in arts, sciences and the whole extent of literature.*

To carry out his instructions, a sum of eight thousand pounds sterling was at the disposal of the trustees. He directed also that any profit accruing from the sale of these books should go to the authors.

Sir Charles Bell was among the first eight selected to write. As a result this classic in anatomy was published in 1834, in London, by William Pickering. It is done in an excellent style and is the best of the group, scientifically speaking. Bell was a professor of anatomy at the Royal College of Surgeons and a member of their council. He had great artistic abilities as well as an understanding of anatomical problems. His contributions, especially in neurology, were comparable to those of Harvey and should be known to those whose livelihood rests in the fields of the life sciences.

These Bridgewater treatises are far more enlightening than any modern attempt by the orthodox to instill in the reader a belief in and homage towards God.

42. JEAN BAPTISTE PIERRE ANTOINE DE MONET, CHEVALIER DE LAMARCK: *Philosophie Zoologique*

In order to know what Lamarck actually said, one should read him first hand; there have been many editions since his zoological philosophy was first printed in 1809. There are two very good treatises which aid in understanding Lamarck. One is Marcel Landrieu's *Lamarck, le fondateur du transformisme, Sa vie, son oeuvre*, published as Tome XXI of the *Mémoires de la Société Zoologique de France* in 1909 in Paris. The second is a shorter and more authoritative book, *Lamarck*, by Edmond Perrier, in *Les Grands Hommes de France,* published in Paris in 1926 by Payot.

In 1963 an English translation of this work, *Zoological Philosophy,* was published by Hafner Publishing Co., New York and London. The translation, with an introduction, was by Hugh Elliot.

43. CHARLES LYELL: *Principles of Geology, Being an Attempt to Explain the Former Changes of the Earth's Surface by Reference to Causes Now in Operation*

This book is more than the study of geology. Lyell's knowledge of biology was profound. A close friend of Darwin and finally one of his supporters, he had been up to the time of the publication of the *Origin of Species* an anti-transformationist, but upon its publication he immediately became a Darwinian. Lyell's account of biology gives an insight as to how far evolutionary thinking had progressed before Darwin. There have been many editions. The first edition of 1830 is suggested in order to get the full benefit of the historical perspective; one of the later editions after 1859 will throw light on Lyell's thinking about evolutionary problems. All editions were published by John Murray of London.

44. CHARLES ROBERT DARWIN: *Origin of Species*

This great classic needs no comment except that it and the works of Sigmund Freud and Karl Marx have revolutionized the thinking of mankind. Copies of later editions should be read for comparison with the first, since this will give the student an insight into how Darwin changed his thinking concerning certain concepts.

45. FRANCIS GALTON: *Natural Inheritance*

Since our selection deals primarily with man and his relation to the universe, no more fitting book on man's natural inheritance, historically speaking, could be recommended. Recent techniques dealing with man's biological heredity are more refined, but basic principles were first elucidated by Galton. All students of human behavior, no matter what their specialty, will benefit by reading this great classic. The book was published in London and New York in 1889 by Macmillan.

46. AUGUST WEISMANN: *Essays upon Heredity and Kindred Biological Problems*

These essays constitute a landmark in the literature of biology. Weismann's treatises on inheritance place Lamarck in proper perspective. They also fill gaps in the knowledge of the period. They were translated and edited by E. B. Poulton, Selmar Schönland, and A. E. Shipley, and published at the Clarendon Press, Oxford, in 1891.

47. WILLIAM MADDOCK BAYLISS: *Principles of General Physiology*

Other authors in the field of physiology could more properly be recommended, since knowledge of the subject is so vast and involved. As an example, the American Physiological Society is publishing a handbook of physiology which will comprise at least ten huge volumes. This, however, is not the purpose of these recommendations. They are primarily presented to give the beginner a broad historical and philosophical base from which to proceed. Bayliss presented general physiology from this point of view, not neglecting fundamentals. He was a general biologist first and a physiologist second.

The original was first published in London in 1915 by Longmans, Green & Co. There have been four editions, the last in 1931.

48. EDMUND B. WILSON: *The Cell in Development and Inheritance*

Modern cytology has advanced greatly since the publication of the third edition of this truly great classic. Nonetheless, as Pearl remarks, "Along with Bayliss' *General Physiology*, just cited, ranks Wilson's *Cell*. In my judgment they are the two best general biological *textbooks* ever written in any language."

The third edition was published with corrections in 1928 in New York by The Macmillan Company.

49. PAUL DE KRUIF: *Microbe Hunters*

Since the publication of Raymond Pearl's *To Begin With,* a whole revolution in microbiology, genetics, and biochemistry has taken place. However, these biographical sketches still stand as insights into the lives of those who preceded the revolution. Probably in no other area of biology have there been such significant breakthroughs as in the origin and nature of life. It will pay the student well to see how the pioneers blazed significant paths into these uncharted regions. There have been 50 printings of this book.

38

A complete and unabridged edition is now available in paperback by Pocket Books, Inc., New York, 1940.

50. ERIK NORDENSKIÖLD: *The History of Biology*

Probably no other book dealing with the general view of the history of biology is as complete and philosophically sound as this one. This work is based on a course of lectures given at the University of Helsinki during the academic year 1916–17. The author presented this history as a link in the general history of culture. It was translated into English by Leonard Bucknall Eyre from its three-volume original *Biologins historia* (1920–1924), and was issued as a new edition by the Tudor Publishing Company, New York, 1935.

CHAPTER FIVE

The nervous system and behavior

Behavior of organisms can be studied profitably without reference to the nervous system, but more fundamental knowledge of behavior (both normal and abnormal) may be obtained if the nervous system is included in the original investigation. This is also true if comparative studies are under consideration. The endocrine systems vitally influence behavior. A few of the suggested readings include the neuroendocrine axis in reference to behavioral studies. These listings indicate clearly the tremendous concern shown in understanding behavior, especially in the last few years. This interest began at the turn of the century, fostered chiefly by the writings of Child, Coghill, and Herrick.

In recent times more and more attention has been given to mental health through private and public support. Whether at the analytically oriented psychiatric level or at the broadly based biological level, the future advance in the field of the behavioral sciences will depend more and more upon a firmer understanding of the nature of the nervous structure and function.

The list in this chapter, it seems to me, will give to the beginner a well-grounded foundation. Included in this list is a book that is unique, Polyak's The Vertebrate Visual System. *It is placed here because it probably contains all the pertinent references that relate to the evolution of the brain, especially that which is related to sight as an influence in the making of the human brain, which, as Herrick says, is the organ of civilization.*

The list, as a whole, in this chapter, is designed to give the reader an insight into the broader view of how brain and behavior are intimately related. It is highly technical; I intended it to be this way. With these as a basis of attack, the young investigator will not only grasp the fundamentals, but he will also be prepared to carry the torch of enlightenment a little farther.

51. MARY A. B. BRAZIER, ED.: *Brain and Behavior*

This is Volume One in a series based on conferences on the brain and behavior, sponsored by the Brain Research Institute, University of California, Los Angeles, in collaboration with the American Institute of Biological Sciences, and with the support of the National Science Foundation. This is a collection of excellent papers that deal with the analysis of the sensory systems—somatic, auditory, and visual. It is logically conceived and brilliantly executed. This area of science is in a crisis. As the co-chairman of the symposium, Dr. Frank Fremont-Smith points out in the Introductory Remarks:

> We are being overwhelmed by so much information, so many data, that we are inclined to limit ourselves to the study of those fragments that fall within our own narrow discipline. New developments of science have repeatedly come through a combined operation of several disciplines in exploring an area which had been previously neglected, an area lying between sharply specialized lines of advance. This conference is an effort to facilitate interdisciplinary communication.

These symposia offer the beginner an insight into the nature of the problems of the brain (central nervous system) and behavior. They bring together current findings of leading investigators from diverse fields bearing on a common problem, behavior, as it can be related to the nervous system. The book was published by the American Institute of Biological Sciences, Washington, D.C., 1961. Quotation used by permission.

52. Eugene L. Bliss: *Roots of Behavior. Genetics, Instinct and Socialization in Animal Behavior*

Much is now being published concerning the nature of behavior, as the listings in this chapter indicate. This symposium, sponsored by the Research Committee of the American Psychiatric Association, does go to the "roots of behavior." The work was published by Harper and Brothers in New York, 1962.

There is no one great book by a single author describing the relationship of brain and behavior; it is yet to be written. Herrick's *Neurological Foundations of Animal Behavior* is the only one of its kind available; hence its inclusion in this list (No. 54).

53. Sir Charles Sherrington: *The Integrative Action of the Nervous System*

This is one of the great classics in neurophysiology and behavior. It was published first in 1906 by Charles Scribner's Sons. The present edition is the second, published by the Yale University Press, 1948, New Haven.

54. C. Judson Herrick: *Neurological Foundations of Animal Behavior*

Two books concerned with the fundamental mechanics of behavior appeared simultaneously in 1924, published by Henry Holt & Company of New York. They were this one and another by C. M. Child entitled *Physiological Foundations of*

Behavior. Both now appear as reprints by the Hafner Publishing Co., New York: Herrick's in 1962 and Child's in 1963. The two men, Child and Herrick, co-operated with one another to bring before the scientific world a reasonably comprehensive perspective of the intrinsic structure-function relationships of behavior. Child's treatment was more inclusive, while Herrick stressed neuronal mechanisms and patterns.

The cathode-ray oscilloscope was at this time (1920's) becoming a workable tool in neurophysiological studies. The presentation of these neurological and physiological foundations of behavior was timely and in a sense timeless. The high degree of present-day sophistication in electronic gear only confirms or extends slightly the original information contained in these two classics. Students of behavior are of necessity continually exploring the underlying mechanisms of behavior. Because of the rational approach towards the physical organization of living systems at any of their levels, the information as given in these books certainly will silence forever any entelechies or metaphysical daemons that attempt to raise their ghastly heads to blur the clear picture here presented.

55. C. JUDSON HERRICK: *Brains of Rats and Men.* *A survey of the origin and biological significance of the cerebral cortex*

H. L. Mencken, in reviewing this book, remarked that it was the best account in the English language relating to this subject. With this I agree. Many details have since been added, but it must be stressed that for a clear general view of the comparative study it still ranks first.

At a recognition dinner given in honor of Professor Herrick's 25 years of service with the University of Chicago, he made this facetious remark: "If any of you younger people desire to become famous you should write a book entitled

Brains of Cats and Women." The book has not yet been written.

Herrick's book was originally published by the University of Chicago Press. It has recently been reprinted by the Hafner Publishing Company, New York, 1963.

56. *Neurophysiology of Learning and Behavior:*
A symposium held in Chicago, April 12, 1960.
In Memoriam: C. Judson Herrick 1868–1960.
Sponsored by the American Physiological Society

Professor W. R. Adey, in his contribution to this symposium, "Brain Mechanisms and the Learning Process," paid this tribute to Dr. Herrick:

> In paying homage to the memory of Charles Judson Herrick, the neurophysiologist and neuroanatomist is confronted with a herculean task. For this man demands no prosaic elegy, no perfunctory appraisal of good research neatly contrived and meticulously executed. Indubitably, all this was his, and yet there was much more to the mighty frame in which he lived and worked. It is surely not too much to say that he has made for himself, in the truly epic quality of his research, a place amongst the immortals.

Professor Herrick was to have been honorary chairman of this symposium. He died January 28, 1960, two and a half months before the symposium was held. His paper, "Nervous Mechanisms of Behavior," the last one he wrote, was read at this conference by Dr. Robert B. Livingston and was included in the conference publication.

Several reasons come to mind for the inclusion of this symposium. First, Herrick's own paper at the age of 92 is an inspiration. Second, this symposium, as a tribute to Herrick, says what I could not say for fear of being accused of hero worship. Third, it shows clearly that great men do work alone without the benefit of a battery of assistants and gadgets. Fourth, the papers presented here clearly reveal the present state of our knowledge and technological skills in this exciting area of brain and behavior.

This symposium appeared in volume 20, part 1, pages 601 to 631 of the Federation of American Societies for Experimental Biology, July, 1961.

57. G. E. W. WOLSTENHOLME AND CECILIA M. O. CONNOR, EDS.: *Ciba Foundation Symposium* on the *Neurological Basis of Behaviour, in Commemoration of Sir Charles Sherrington*

A symposium in its pristine sense is defined as a drinking party. If one calls the roll of those attending the international conferences from which emerge these impressive tomes, one soon discovers that some notable participants are listed on each panel. I am sure that these sturdy souls are resistant to the heady wines of several behavioral vintages and are valiant in dispensing their own brew. This is truly laudable, for we see that there is always a slight difference in the aroma that meets the olfactory mucosa with each new setting of the wine glasses.

Actually, each symposium carries a different emphasis. I list these important landmarks in world neurobehavioral opinion on the basis that they are focal points in present-day thinking. They are the seed beds from which new ideas spring.

Little, Brown and Company of Boston published this in 1958.

58. ANNE ROE AND GEORGE GAYLORD SIMPSON, EDS.: *Behavior and Evolution*

Two large groups of American scientists, the American Psychological Association and the Society for the Study of Evolution, pooled their talents and efforts to bring together basic knowledge relative to the evolution of behavior. Up until recently psychological study of behavior lacked a sound evolutionary basis. Evolutionary study at the purely biological level likewise was lacking in behavioral components. We have now, in this interdisciplinary approach, taken steps to rectify these weaknesses. As a result we have in these excellent essays a beginning of an exciting and profitable approach to the behavior of the fauna of this little planet.

All students who in any way will be dealing with life processes should familiarize themselves with the basic principles of behavior. This collection of essays affords an excellent start for a lifetime of exciting adventures, as one begins to understand how a big-brained primate like himself got to be the way he is.

These essays were published by the Yale University Press, New Haven, 1958.

59. Harry F. Harlow and Clinton N. Woolsey, eds.: *Biological and Biochemical Bases of Behavior*

Interdisciplinary scientific enterprises are slowly becoming the order of the day. At the present time no one person or even a small group of men is sufficiently gifted or equipped to completely fathom and to delve deeply into all of the intricacies of the brain in its entirety, relative to meaningful behavioral patterns. However, once new information is available, the pieces of the jigsaw puzzle can be assembled by those who have familiarity with the general view. Symposia permit not only the presentation of various bits of information but also aid in their assembly into understandable wholes. This symposium is one in which many diverse fields are brought to bear upon most functional levels of the brain and behavior.

The University of Wisconsin Press at Madison published this book in 1958.

60. H. C. SOLOMON, STANLEY COBB, AND WILDER PENFIELD, EDS.: *The Brain and Human Behavior*

Again, this is a symposium; this time, however, in the form of the proceedings of The Association for Research in Nervous and Mental Diseases, constituting Volume 36 in this excellent series. It was published in 1958 by the Williams and Wilkins Company, Baltimore.

I recommend this primarily because of its high quality of scientific essays. Special attention should be given to K. S. Lashley's "Cerebral Organization and Behavior" and Wilder Penfield's "Functional Localization in Temporal and Deep Sylvian Areas."

The young scientist who elects to enter the medical field will find in these essays excellent examples of neurological literature. All students who are concerned with human behavior will profit greatly by these incisive papers.

61. MARY A. B. BRAZIER, ED.: *The Central Nervous System and Behavior*

This work consists of the transactions of the first, second, and third conferences of The Josiah Macy, Jr., Foundation, a part of multi-professional discussions of current research in medicine 1958, 1959, 1960.

Few people can go contrary to the cultural trend in which they move. The modern scientific intellectual tends to become more and more gregarious; fewer and fewer scientists are "lone" laboratory workers. Consequently, we have more published works of symposia instead of books by individual scholars. Even the "lone" scientist now has a corps of research assistants—many of them subsidized by federal or private agencies. The results of the managerial scientist's labor seem to flow more easily into published accounts assembled into transactions of the conferences in which he so usefully operates.

I am not deploring this course of events. As a matter of fact, I have engaged in such behavior.

The conferences of which we speak were sponsored and the results published by The Josiah Macy, Jr., Foundation, with the co-operation of The National Science Foundation, Washington, D.C. There were three annual conferences concerned in this undertaking with three corresponding publications. Previous to the second and third conference, The National Institutes of Health, through its Russian Scientific Translation Program, translated, assembled, and published recent relevant Russian scientific studies for the benefit of the participants at these conferences. This study is probably one of the largest undertakings of its kind in the field of behavior as it is related to the nervous system.

It should be emphasized that the guiding light in this enterprise was Horace W. Magoun, Professor of Anatomy, and now Dean of the Graduate School, U.C.L.A. He more than anyone else, except perhaps his loyal helper, Dr. Mary Brazier, engineered the project. He was chairman at all three conferences.

The neophyte in the field of the nervous system as it is related to behavior can ill afford to overlook this rich source of information. It is presented primarily as an example, in good taste, of the trend in our "modern" scientific culture.

62. GEORGE ELLETT COGHILL: *Anatomy and the Problem of Behaviour*

No other embryologist has contributed information with such penetrating insight into the basic problems of behavior as the late Professor Coghill. In this little book, which consists of three lectures, delivered at Cambridge University and published by its press in 1929, he relates the sequence of events that occur in the orderly development of behavior of the salamander. For the first time scientists were able to understand how total patterns of behavior (integration) dominated and controlled partial patterns of behavior (reflexes) which Coghill called analytical. Through the use of Coghill's basic concepts, C. Judson Herrick was able to formulate his ideas on the origins of human mentation, and from this evolve his concepts of the evolution of human nature, all of which is mentioned in other references in this book.

An urgent note concerning Coghill is in order: He was trained primarily as a psychologist interested in philosophy. Before undertaking his lifelong scientific work, he made sure of his approach. He spent several months on the deserts of the Southwest wrestling with himself and turning over in his mind how best to approach the problem of mental life or mentation. He decided the best way was to see how behavior developed. He could not have picked a more suitable animal on which to work. Psychologists, psychiatrists (both analytically and biologically oriented), philosophers, and physiologists—all have benefitted from this embryological approach.

The idea of conflict between the integrative and the analytical aspects of the nervous system had its first expression in Coghill.

This little classic is reprinted by the Hafner Publishing Co., New York, 1964.

63. I. P. PAVLOV: *Conditioned Reflexes. An Investigation of the Physiological Activity of the Cerebral Cortex*

No other book concerned with neurophysiology plus its implications has had a more profound impact on world thought and on the behavior of man than this great classic. The leaders of education in the Soviet Union have taken too seriously Pavlov's teachings and have made them basic to their educational techniques and ideology, forgetting the warnings offered by the master in these words:

Obviously even greater caution must be used in attempting similarly to apply our recently acquired knowledge concerning the higher nervous activity in the dog—the more so, since the incomparably greater development of the cerebral cortex in man is pre-eminently that factor which has raised man to his dominant position in the animal world. It would be the height of presumption to regard these first steps in elucidating the physiology of the cortex as solving the intricate problems of the higher psychic activities in man, when in fact at the present stage of our work no detailed application of its results to man is yet permissible.

Modern Soviet neurophysiologists who have brought their science to its present world position seemed to be compelled to overdo or stretch the Pavlovian principles, as other biologists were compelled to pay homage to Lysenko under Stalin.

The book was translated and edited by G. V. Anrept, a former collaborator with Pavlov. Pavlov says: "Dr. Anrept's task has not been an easy one, and it has been fraught with responsibility, as practically at every step he has had to adapt a vast new terminology. I wish to give him also my hearty thanks."

It first appeared in 1927 at the Oxford University Press, but an excellent paperback reproduction has been published by the Dover Publications, Inc., New York, 1960.

64. K. S. LASHLEY: *Brain Mechanisms and Intelligence*

This is one of the truly great books on physiological psychology. Man has always been extremely curious about his own mysterious nature. To understand the nature of man's mind (intelligence), Lashley approached the problem indirectly through the rat. The inferences drawn are in the main quite applicable to all primates, including man.

The original book was published by the University of Chicago Press in 1929. Hafner Publishing Company of New York has a recent reprint, 1964.

65. STEPHEN POLYAK: *The Vertebrate Visual System.*
   Its origin, structure, and function and its
   manifestations in disease with an analysis of its role
   in the life of animals and in the origin of man,
   preceded by a historical review of investigations of
   the eye and of the visual pathways and centers
   of the brain

Professor Polyak died before his great book was published. His good friend and colleague, Heinrich Klüver, took two years out of his productive life to edit this great masterpiece of neurological literature. It is included here because it is one of the finest attempts to place man in a naturalistic setting. In the epilogue, one reads about the place of sight in the evolutionary scheme of things in man's long struggle to be human. Sight has had more to do in shaping the primate brain than any other modality. This book will remain an outstanding reference work. It was published by the University of Chicago Press, 1957.

CHAPTER SIX

Man and the universe

This is probably a weak title for a chapter dealing with such an involved subject. The readings suggested here are few, almost infinitesimal when compared with all the books that have been written concerning the central theme of man's existence. These books attempt to portray man's place in nature. Many such attempts to depict a unitary principle in physics and biology have been made. I will discuss this later when I consider Lancelot Law Whyte's The Unitary Principle in Physics and Biology. *The suggestions here are on a broad plane; they are offered in an attempt to place man in as comprehensive a view as is presently possible from our existing information. These books present this view admirably well.*

66. CHARLES ROBERT DARWIN: *The Descent of Man*

This great classic belongs at the head of any list of recommended books on man. For a discussion of this book, see No. 77, in the chapter that follows.

67. MARK TWAIN (SAMUEL CLEMENS): *What Is Man?*

This essay in no way represents the literary genius of one of America's great authors. In fact, as literature it probably would be regarded as one of Twain's poorest. Mark Twain firmly believed the universe to be absolutely, unwaveringly determined, as he clearly points out in this essay and so vividly portrays in his great classics, *Tom Sawyer* and *Huckleberry*

Finn. One who becomes a Mark Twain fan cannot stop until he has read most of his writings—particularly *The Mysterious Stranger. What Is Man?* is suggested here not necessarily as a philosophical treatise on free will or determinism, but to help introduce our section on man and the universe, for it brings the question down to earth more than any single essay with which I am familiar.

Mark Twain's works have gone through many editions and printings. The Stormfield Edition published by Harper & Brothers, New York, 1929, is one of the better ones.

68. W. MACNEILE DIXON: *The Human Situation*

There are very few books that present the human situation as vividly in its stark reality as Dixon's. Nor are there other authors who can so reasonably and wholesomely, "with sparkling wit, apt allusion and happy analogy," counteract the harsh truths which the world presents. Possibly this book should be placed among the books related to religious principles; but on further consideration, it probably belongs in this chapter, which attempts to look at the human situation in its totality. The essays in the book were delivered as the Gifford Lectures at the University of Glasgow in 1935–1937 and are now available in paperback as a Galaxy Book, Oxford University Press, New York, 1958.

69. ALEXANDER POPE. *Essay on Man. In Four Epistles to H. St. John, Lord Bolingbroke*

This essay-poem constitutes one of the masterpieces of eighteenth-century poetry. However, it is not included here for literary reasons, but as an example of the thought processes of our Anglo-American culture. It is not placed here to counteract Mark Twain; no doubt Twain would have great fun spoofing much of what Pope said about man's relation to nature and to God. The poem may be obtained from many editions and through anthologies. The recommended edition was edited by A. Hamilton Thompson and was published at the University Press, Cambridge, in 1913.

70. HARLOW SHAPLEY: *Of Stars and Men—Human Response to an Expanding Universe*

For sheer joy and insight into the study of the nature of things in the modern world, Harlow Shapley's *Of Stars and Men* presents a panoramic, cosmic view of the known universe that is breathtaking. It is a story told by the former director of the Harvard Observatory in a manner that is not too technical but which is accurate in details. As is evident in many of these suggested readings, time and space play extensive roles in the ordering of the patterns of existence. *Of Stars and Men* exemplifies well these two aspects of nature. The book was published by the Beacon Press, Boston, 1958.

71. PIERRE TEILHARD DE CHARDIN: *The Phenomenon of Man*

This is an unusual book—unusual because it was written by a great Jesuit paleontologist in spite of the Church's denunciation of it. Pierre Teilhard de Chardin was a remarkable man. He was in pursuit of truth, and where it led him he followed. What he had to say about man's place in nature is sound, but he goes far beyond the bounds of the scientific when he mixes his sincere religious views with his science. He introduces many new words and thoughts in his phenomenalizing of man. His great contribution is his ability to unify the picture of cosmic evolution. He did this with consummate skill, with elegance. If one overlooks his concern with religious implications, there exist few other books or treatises which place man so completely in the phenomenal world. This is mysticism in its simplest and purest form.

The book was first published in French as *Le Phénomène Humain,* in Paris, 1955, by Editions du Seuil. In 1959, it was published in English by William Collins Sons & Co., London, and by Harper & Row, New York (Torchbooks); it was translated by Bernard Wall with an excellent introduction by Julian Huxley.

72. JAN CHRISTIAN SMUTS: *Holism and Evolution*

General Smuts was one of the world's great statesmen, whose country, South Africa, failed to listen to his teachings or follow the path upon which he had placed it; nevertheless, he will long be remembered by this fundamental treatment of the evolutionary process. Whitehead gave us a modern view of science without the inclusive syntheses expressed by Herrick, Smuts, or Teilhard de Chardin. In the hands of Smuts all nature is described as having built within her a "whole-making" technique. He states that "evolution is nothing but the gradual development and stratification of a progressive series of wholes stretching from the inorganic beginnings to the highest levels of spiritual creation." General Smuts' *Holism and Evolution* presents a philosophical and naturalistic interpretation of nature, devoid of any vitalistic tinge.

The book was originally published by The Macmillan Company, New York, 1926, but has recently been reprinted by the Viking Press, New York, 1961, as a paperback in their Compass Books Edition.

73. LOREN EISELEY: *The Immense Journey*

Few men are gifted naturalists as well as poets. Loren Eiseley is one of those unusual specimens of Homo sapiens whose superb talents as a scientist are combined with subtle abilities for poetic expression. The result of this combination is the production of such a rare piece of fascinating scientific literature as *The Immense Journey,* published by Random House, New York, in 1946, with six subsequent printings. The universe abounds with mystery. Loren Eiseley explores the mystery of man and nature with delicate aplomb. Few books will leave the reader more enchanted than *The Immense Journey.* Using the technique of Bacon, who really saw through time, Eiseley paints a portrait of man's journey through time and space with deft strokes on a wide canvas. He makes man more mysterious than ever before.

Eiseley's account of the lives of Darwin's predecessors in a book entitled *Darwin's Century* should not be overlooked by students of biology. In this book the reader will find in Chapter XI Eiseley's account of "Wallace and The Brain," which is a superb consideration of the most controversial points between Darwin and Wallace. Once you have read Eiseley, you will be determined to read all that he has written. Two more of his books worth mentioning are *The Firmament of Time* and *Francis Bacon and the Modern Dilemma.*

74. C. Judson Herrick: *The Evolution of Human Nature*

Probably no other book which relates the development and function of the brain in its relationship to human behavior will give the reader as much pleasure and valuable insight into man's potentialities as Herrick's *magnum opus,* published when he was 88 years old. This book had its beginning in an unpublished manuscript entitled *The Nature and Origins of Human Mentation* (this essay was published posthumously in *World Neurology,* Vol. 2, pp. 1028–1045, 1961). The essay was expanded into two unpublished manuscripts, *The Evolution of Behavior* and *The Evolution of Brains.* These two manuscripts were finally combined into the book's present form and published by the University of Texas Press in Austin, 1956. This delightfully penetrating account of man's struggle to be human was so popular that a paperback edition is now available in the Science Library, published by Harper and Brothers, New York, in the Torchbooks Series of 1961. C. Judson Herrick was a scientist whose chief quest was the natural history of the human spirit. From this he never wavered. He spent 70 years fathoming the intricate neural complication of the salamander brain (see his *Brain of the Tiger Salamander,* University of Chicago Press, 1948). There are three vertebrate brains on this planet about which more is known than about any other brains. They are the brains of the salamander, the rat, and man. Herrick had everything to do with one, and much to do with the other two. In looking over the long natural history of brains found on this little planet earth, no greater exhilaration can be found than that expressed in Chapter XVIII of the book entitled *The Spiritual Life of a Mechanist.* I include two other books by Herrick in this reading list, because of his profound insight into what brains do in organizing and executing behavior. From these three books, the reader will see clearly the maturation of thinking in a great naturalist—probably nowhere else so vividly portrayed.

CHAPTER SEVEN

Mathematics of biology

As I indicated for biology: what was recommended was only a beginning. So too what will be said of mathematics, as applied to biology, will constitute only an introduction. I have left out many technical treatises; once the beginning student is on his way with some knowledge of the basic patterns of thinking, he can easily master the technicalities. Since one of the chief concerns of this total list is that which deals with the nervous system and behavior, it is only fitting that recommendations concerning the "logic" of neurology should be included.

No attempt will be made to introduce the student to the "new math." He will have been exposed long before he reads this. The chapter on biostatistics in Pearl's To Begin With *was primarily concerned with vital statistics. In* Let Us Start Here, *I have tried to present a broader aspect, calling attention to the involvement of computers as they are slowly yet effectively aiding in solving problems in biology, their use ranging from mathematical taxonomy to that which aids in understanding the structure and function of the human brain.*

Nature is a very conservative mother. The basic molecular reactions used in genetic information probably are the same intrinsic ones at work in memory mechanisms. It is imperative that we fathom these codes. It is clear that mathematics is the most likely tool used in the solving of these ever-appearing problems.

58

75. JOHN GRAUNT: *Natural and Political Observations Mentioned in a Following Index, and Made Upon the Bills of Mortality, 1662*

In presenting this broad subject, one turns to the first outstanding treatise which relates mathematics to human vital phenomena. C. H. Hull's *The Economic Writings of Sir William Petty,* etc. (Cambridge: The University Press, 1899) contains a well-edited and well-annotated reprint of this classic.

76. THOMAS ROBERT MALTHUS: *Essay on the Principle of Population as It Affects the Future Improvement of Society*

Malthus was a very popular writer, and Darwin spoke of him as a "great philosopher." Darwin wrote a note to himself: "Study Malthus and calculate rates of increase [for various species]." The views of Malthus acted as "a catalyst in the final precipitation of Darwin's thought." The geometric growth of life expressed by Malthus made a deep impression on Darwin, and it is possible that this turned his thoughts more intensively upon the struggle for existence. This is clearly indicated in Darwin's essay of 1842. Malthus was the impelling force that buoyed the Darwinian principle in the struggle for existence. This great classic can be found in the Everyman Library Edition, which is a reprint of the seventh edition of the original work. It should be pointed out that each edition is different, so a collector might wish to have all editions. This was last printed in 1952.

77. CHARLES ROBERT DARWIN: *The Descent of Man*

I repeat this book here for obvious reasons. Probably no more burning question exists in biology than the one "Who are we?"

Many astonomers and physicists, and some biochemists, assume that once life arises on a planet, it is almost inevitable that man will appear as we know him on our own. This assumption is probably false, for it suggests that in all details the evolutionary processes would be identical to our own. This leaves us with the idea that we are alone in the vastness of the universe as far as consciousness of our own existence is concerned. To my mind, no better beginning than Darwin's treatment of this subject exists. How-did-we-get-this-way should intrigue all intelligent and inquisitive men and women.

The Descent of Man can be purchased in many editions. *The Origin of Species* (sixth edition, 1872) and *The Descent of Man* were published in The Modern Library, New York.

Much has taken place since 1872, the year Darwin published *The Descent of Man,* in the way of new finds, more exact geological timing, etc. I mention only two books related to these discoveries: L. S. B. Leakey's *Adam's Ancestors: The Evolution of Man and His Culture,* Harper Torchbooks, The Academy Library—Harper Brothers, New York, 1960; and *Mankind in the Making: The Story of Human Evolution,* by William White Howells, Doubleday & Co., New York, 1959. Both of these clearly give the recent status of man's evolutionary condition.

78. ALFRED NORTH WHITEHEAD: *An Introduction to Mathematics*

In *To Begin With* (Alfred A. Knopf, Inc., 1927), Raymond Pearl wrote:

> This little treatise published in 1911 in the *Home University Library* series (New York, Henry Holt & Co.) has served admirably two useful purposes in my laboratory ever since its appearance. First to dispel mathematicophobia when present, and second to demonstrate to the average student fresh from

undergraduate mathematics, as taught in our colleges and universities, that the intellectual content of the subject extends beyond puzzle-solving.

I have expressed the profound impact made by Whitehead's *Science and the Modern World.* His mathematical genius was of a similar nature. With Bertrand Russell he published *Principia mathematica.* Later his interests changed to more philosophical problems—problems initiated by contemporary science. Coming to America, Whitehead began a new career at Harvard. His metaphysical writings were obscure to the philosophical fraternity. However, he may eventually be considered not only a forerunner but also one of the founders of a new school, yet unnamed, which is attempting to unify what we know and what we can know about the universe of which we are intimately a part.

79. Isaac Todhunter: *A History of the Mathematical Theory of Probability from the Time of Pascal to That of Laplace*

As in every discipline there must be a basic reference—a sort of Bible, as Pearl would say, to which students return with reverence. This selection is such a book. It was first published in 1865, in Cambridge and London by Macmillan. It is no longer available but can be found in most university libraries.

80. Francis Galton: *Inquiries into Human Faculty and Its Development*

Galton's greatest contribution to science was his correlational calculus, in which new statistical methods were devised. However, he is best known as the initiator of the study of eugenics. His extensive family records enabled him to assess heredity quantitatively by a correlation of physical and mental characteristics. His interest in anthropometry led him to recognize

61

that two characters measured on an organism are associated, rather than independent.

Raymond Pearl was prone to a certain degree of hero worship. Galton stands "serene in the center of the galaxy" in Pearl's hierarchy of immortals. The book can be found in Everyman's Library (E. P. Dutton, New York).

81. J. LOTTIN: *Quetelet: Statisticien et Sociologue*

Quetelet is one of the eventful links in the history of vital statistics which binds its present-day practitioners with Laplace, since he was a student of the latter. Historically it is important that we get a glimpse of this man, not that he was one of the immortals in the field, but it was he who organized the first international statistical conference. He was also a developer of uniformity and comparability in international statistics. In his study he applied the probability theory to anthropology and sociology. Statistical science, through Lambert Quetelet, was placed on a firm foundation. Lottin's life of Quetelet appeared in Louvain and Paris in 1912 (Alcan).

82. CHARLES SANTIAGO SANDERS PEIRCE: *A Theory of Probable Inference*

Peirce may well be called the father of Pragmatism; although he did not call it that, he is known to have originated the word as well as the idea. The book is a classic. Anyone who deals with the theory of probable inference cannot be called well-trained unless he has mastered the contents of this truly exciting essay. It also will pay handsomely to those who are concerned with the unitary principle in physics and biology to look into Peirce's studies of psychophysics; a beginner in the field which is now depicting the strategy of life will find his psychophysics useful, for "conscious strategy of man is a necessary sequel to the strategy of life."

This essay appeared originally in *Studies in Logic by Members of the Johns Hopkins University*, pp. 126–181, Little, Brown & Company, 1883, Boston.

83. WILLIAM FARR: *Vital Statistics: A Memorial Volume of Selections from the Reports and Writings of William Farr, M.D., D.C.L., C.B., F.P.S.*, Edited by Noel A. Humphreys

Pearl recommends that one should supplement his reading from William Farr's selections by delving deeper into the Registrar General's Reports from which Humphreys obtained these originals, for Humphreys did not exhaust the valuable material therein. Pearl speaks of Farr as being "the greatest medical statistician who has lived." The book was published by the Sanitary Institute of Great Britain (London, 1885) as a memorial to Farr.

84. KNUD FABER: *Nosography in Modern Internal Medicine*

Many readers of *Let Us Start Here* may be concerned with exact medical nomenclature. Faber's book is misleading in that it is not a history of medicine but of medical ideas. The World Health Organization's *Manual of International Statistical Classification of Diseases, Injuries and Causes of Death* (7th revision of *International Lists of Diseases*, 1957) is, however, a universally accepted list of diseases numerically labeled for exactness for the programming of problems given to computers.

The *Nosography* was published by Humphrey Milford, Oxford University Press, in London, 1923.

85. WILLIAM BOYD: *A Textbook of Pathology: An Introduction to Modern Medicine*

For those who will become practicing vital-statisticians, a modern text describing pathological states is almost a must, since the World Health Organization's classifications of causes of death should at least be understood. For those who will be concerned with neurological problems, a general text of pathology will be basic. This book was published by Lea & Febiger, Philadelphia, 1961.

86. JAMES V. NEEL AND WILLIAM J. SCHULL: *Human Heredity*

There are a number of excellent books on human heredity. It would require many huge tomes for even the beginning of a summary concerning our knowledge and our techniques of this important subject. This book by Neel and Schull comes as close to my purpose of introducing genetics in relation to man as any with which I am familiar. The book emphasizes methodology as opposed to basic human genetic information. It was published by the University of Chicago Press (second impression) in 1957.

87. GEORGE UDNY YULE: *An Introduction to the Theory of Statistics*

This selection presents, as Pearl states it, "a sound, well ripened philosophy of the statistical method." Much has happened in the science of statistics since the appearance of this book. It is included for its wisdom and historical position.

The seventh edition was published by Griffin (London) in 1924.

88. John von Neumann: *The General and Logical Theory of Automata*

In the strategy of life it now becomes clear that organisms (man included) are self-regulating machines, each geared to re-create its likeness with undeviating regularity, except under the selective pressure of the environment, when variations may occur, permitting the newer forms to take advantage of the changing surroundings. This latter is called mutation. In man, the nervous system (i.e., the master tissue assigned to this organismic self-regulation) has reached its highest complexity. One man who has contributed much to this problem of self-regulation is John von Neumann. This article was one of his first attempts at solutions. Its setting was unique; he was the only nonbiologist present at the Hixon Symposium, discussing cerebral mechanisms in behavior.

Von Neumann's attack on the problems of automata continued, culminating in the publication, posthumously by his wife, of the intriguing little book *The Computer and the Brain*, which actually was an elaboration of an earlier essay, *The General and Logical Theory of Automata*. In this essay we see how valuable mathematics can be when applied to such problems as self-regulation (either natural or artificial). This essay appeared as the first article in *Cerebral Mechanisms in Behavior*, The Hixon Symposium, pp. 1–41, 1951, edited by Lloyd Jeffress, John Wiley & Sons, Inc., New York.

89. J. Z. Young: *A Model of the Brain*

The simplest nerve net is a highly complicated mechanism. I have selected J. Z. Young's admirable treatise on the octopus brain for the chief reason that it portrays a model—a model of an invertebrate brain that has reached the peak of invertebrate brain evolution. A model is an extremely beautiful and useful tool designed by man to explain many features of the natural world. Young says this in a more meaningful and direct way:

> The biologist is endlessly curious about the details of living activity and structure. His interest in animals and plants is held because he finds these details satisfying. His value to the biological technologies is again in his knowledge of these facts. Why then be concerned with all this talk about models? Has the introduction of the theme throughout this book done any more than obscure the facts and irritate those who wish to know what the author has found out? I will confess that I often have doubts, being myself fascinated, indeed obsessed, by the beauty and interest of the structure and function of the nervous system.
>
> Yet this beauty is far enhanced when attention to it seems to lead to something that we have called "understanding" of how the nervous system works. This experience in turn has led to exciting problems of what is meant by "understanding" and by "function." Equally exciting is the discovery that one can play a part in the process of model building itself, producing artifacts that are both interesting and useful. Models themselves have great beauty. It is true that theirs is only a dim representation of the glories of the world around. But without them how else are we to know these beauties . . . ?

Model building in brain function and structure demands a mathematical approach if one carries his workmanship to a sophisticated level. J. Z. Young does this to a limited extent. He has paved the way for great advancement in this area, the beginning of the cybernetic age.

This book is the result of The William Withering Lectures, delivered to the faculty of medicine at the University of Birmingham, in 1960, under the title "Mechanisms of Learning and Form Discrimination." It was published by the Clarendon Press, Oxford, 1964, which permitted the quotations.

66

90. Ralph W. Stacy and Bruce D. Waxman:
Computers in Biomedical Research

There is no doubt that the development of the use of computers in biomedical sciences represents one of the major contributions to science in this century. There are no delineative publications in this field. The fifty contributors to these two volumes are leaders in their respective fields. The work represents diverse interests, as it should; hence it is directed to a wide audience, which includes all the biomedical sciences, both "pure" and "applied." The all-inclusive coverage includes computer technology, broad concepts of application to biomedical problems, descriptions of specific research programs, and "even in a few cases some projection of things to come." There is in this array of material a highly sophisticated application of computers to highly discrete biosciences as well as some of the naïve everyday uses.

The English have been more businesslike and more coherent in matters of computers in biology and medicine than have their American counterparts, as shown in a recent publication, *Mathematics and Computer Science in Biology and Medicine,* published by Her Majesty's Stationery Office. The British book is the result of the Medical Research Council's proceedings. The two books are largely complementary. Both volumes were edited by Ralph W. Stacy and Bruce D. Waxman, published by the Academic Press, New York, 1965.

In a recent issue of *Science* (Vol. 151, pp. 969–972), a National Academy of Science Panel calls for more federal aid to extend the use of computers on college campuses. The use of computers has skyrocketed in the last few years, and the end is not in sight. The undergraduate in many areas is being trained in computer science. Computers are to space-time-biological problems what telescopes are to astronomy, or what microscopes are to biology.

67

The "biometry" of bygone times is now enhanced by computer technology in the hands of skilled programmers. This explosive technology in no sense will replace the biometrician, for mathematics applied to biology is itself forging new concepts, new applications.

CHAPTER EIGHT

The strategy of life

In the days of Sputnik, Mercury, Gemini, and Apollo space-crafts, we are bombarded with notions concerning the presence of manlike creatures throughout the universe. Fred Hoyle, England's astronomer royal, in a series of lectures at the University of Washington, in Seattle, recently contended that throughout the universe there are at least a billion habitable planets revolving around the trillions of suns that compose our universe. He even suggested that we get our name in the Galactic Telephone Directory so we can start communicating with one another. He does not suggest how the messages will be coded nor what the recipients will do in sending back answers to that part of the universe from which the original dispatch was sent more than a million light-years previously.

Most biologists take a more realistic view concerning the presence of manlike organisms in the universe. We are almost assured by the findings of Mariner IV's voyage to Mars that there exist no highly developed forms of life in our own solar system, other than on our own planet, earth. Dr. George Gaylord Simpson in This View of Life (Harcourt, Brace & World, Inc., New York, 1964) has this to say about the presence of hominoid creatures other than those found on earth:

> The assumption, so freely made by astronomers, physicists, and some biochemists, that once life gets started anywhere, humanoids will eventually and inevitably appear is plainly false. The chance of duplicating man on any other planet is the same as the chance that the planet and its organisms have had a his-

tory identical in all essentials with that of the earth through some billions of years. Let us grant the unsubstantiated claim of millions or billions of possible planetary abodes of life; the chances of such historical duplication are still vanishingly small.

Our concern in this chapter is the strategy by which life as we know it succeeded in bringing the earth's biota to its present state, with emphasis on man's unique position in it.

The expression "from amoeba to man" has significance when viewed in the totality of the universal evolutionary process. There has been strategy based not on any prearranged blueprint but on life's innate mechanisms, naturally fabricated, which in the "nature of things" (De rerum natura) produced the exceedingly diverse and wonderful procession of life forms. This strategy lies within the very nature of all matter, which as we view it today exists at various levels of organization. Each level is highly integrated; otherwise it would not have "survived." This is true for the nucleus of an atom, the atom itself, a simple molecule like water, a highly complex nerve cell, the intricate ant colony, or a great and sprawling nation.

Man's life so far in nature is of extremely short duration. His brain has remained practically unchanged over the last 50,000 years. This brain, however, is the most complicated known mechanism in the universe. That part which sets man above his docile cousins, the great apes, is his enlarged prefrontal lobes so intimately associated with the temporal-parietal complex. This complex, dominated by the prefrontal enlargement, permits man to plan his future, both individually and collectively. How he will continue to go about this planning remains to be seen. The fact that man knows that he possesses this mechanism and grasps something of its functional potential should at least give him hope—a hope which instills a natural exuberance to cope with the unsympathetic and unconcerned universe in which he finds himself.

70

91. C. Judson Herrick: *A Biological Survey of Integrative Levels*

Herrick only hinted, in this essay, at the integrative levels of the inorganic world. The great work on the integrative levels of the inorganic is yet to be written. Lawrence Henderson (No. 4) gave it substance, but much has been learned since his work appeared in 1917. Atomic and nuclear physics have exceedingly enlarged our views of the natural order. Herrick has set the pace for a closer look at integrative mechanisms. One is inclined to say that this is the next big step to be taken by man: to know how "things" became things and remain as such—to know how various levels of existence remain levels. This may be a philosophical question, but the answers are to come from scientists, philosophically oriented. This essay was a part of a collection of essays (pp. 222–242) entitled *Philosophy for the Future: The Quest of Modern Materialism,* edited by Roy Wood Sellers, V. J. McGill, and Marvin Farber and published by The Macmillan Company, New York, 1949.

92. Clifford Grobstein: *The Strategy of Life*

Professor Clifford Grobstein has written a book about biology —really about all the universe of which we are conscious— that puts in a logical, concise, exciting, and most useful form what has been "in the air" for these last few years. I have used his title for the topic of this chapter, for it depicts what I want to convey. He states at the end of his preface:

> From studies diversely aimed at molecules, cells, organisms and populations will come a global conception of earth's biotic film, and from this a projection of this concept to the universe at large. Confidence that we shall achieve this conception also characterizes today's biology. Excitement, confidence, and expectation are in the air, as though all that we now know and say of life is but a prologue.

We know we are on the threshold of an epoch. Our plan to invade space may be unique; our confidence of its success is in no way dimmed by global turmoil. Life's existence of billions of years is now bearing fruit in man's consciousness of his ability to plan his own future, actually pull himself up by his bootstraps. Knowledge is lodged, anchored, directed, and projected by man's brain, chiefly from his frontal lobes. As we begin the cybernetic revolution, we are about to write a new chapter in the book of the cosmos.

How did all this come about? Was it as Hardy expressed it in "Nature's Questionings" from *Collected Poems,* published by The Macmillan Company, New York, 1926?

> We wonder, ever wonder why we find us here!
>> Has some vast Imbecility
>>> Mighty to build and blend,
>>> But impotent to tend
>> Framed us in a jest and left us now to hazardry?
>>> Or come we of an automaton
>>> Unconscious of our pains?
>>> Or are we live remains
>> Of Godhead dying downward, brain and eye now gone?
>>> Or is it some high Plan betides
>>> As yet not understood
>>> Of Evil stormed, by good
>> We the forlorn hope over which achievement strides?

Was it chance, or was it inevitable that given certain circumstances, evolution followed lawful sequences because of the mechanisms involved at all levels of existence? Whose plan was it if there were one? Hindsight is a mirror for the future. *The Strategy of Life* has partial answers to these most pressing and penetrating questions; it tells the story not of the plan or planner, but of a process (evolution in its total cosmic setting): "a steady *creative* progression of life—upon which hindsight confers the appearance of strategy" [italics mine]. The word "strategy" as here used implies an overview, not of detailed

72

tactics, but a cosmic view which involves a nonteleological total process. In no way does it imply or give a balanced summary of biological data. It paints a canvas with large brush strokes, not a fine-lined ink sketch. It is placed here, after Herrick, for the simple reason that although Herrick surveyed this road, it took Grobstein to start construction. There are no "secrets" to life; there are secrets of nature—all nature of which life is only a fleeting part. It portrays the rapid, incisive, penetrating, almost all-inclusive action of the thousands of biochemists, biophysicists, and astronomers to reduce life processes to molecular forms; but it also states very frankly that this is fragmentation. These disciplines are the tools of the scientists describing the "tools" (processes) which life used in strategically making itself manifest in the universal evolutionary ongoing of events. Grobstein makes clear that biology is becoming more and more a logical science. It is for us and those to come to play the game of life of which we are its momentary actors, only a spark in a mighty explosion.

Since man possesses the capacity to look into the future as no other primate can, it behooves him to supply direction and purpose to his development. The conscious strategy of man necessarily follows. Grobstein ends on this last phase, a phase so urgently needed in a world beset with man-made conflicts. The book was published as a paperback by W. H. Freeman & Company, San Francisco, 1965, and the material quoted is used by permission of the publisher.

93. GARRETT HARDIN: *Nature and Man's Fate*

The last chapter of this work, "In Praise of Waste," appeared first in the *Saturday Evening Post,* in 1959, in a series of articles entitled "Adventures of the Mind." The chief concern of Professor Hardin is that nature produces designs without planning or having blueprints available. In regard to this, he says:

Those who have painted pictures of an organized heaven have, implicitly or otherwise, appealed to the esthetic sense in man to try to gain assent to their plans. We know now that a completely planned heaven is either impossible or unbearable. We know that it is not true that design can come only out of planning. Out of luxuriant waste, winnowed by selection, come designs more beautiful and in greater variety than ever man could plan. This is the lesson of Nature that Darwin spelled out for us. Man, now that he makes himself, cannot do better than to emulate Nature's example in allowing for waste and encouraging novelty. There is grandeur in this view of life as a complex of cybernetic systems that produce adaptedness without foresight, design without planning, and progress without dictation. From the simplest means, man, now master of his own fate, may evolve societies of a variety and novelty—yes, even of a beauty—that no man living can now foresee.

And the cybernetic revolution is on its way!!

Nature and Man's Fate was written for the general reader, but I have included it here to illustrate how well a great teacher can make clear the basic scientific biological principles outlined in Grobstein's book. In a very meaningful way this book is an attempt to ascertain the meaning of nature as it affects man's fate. The main emphasis of my list, of course, is not only the emancipation of the mind but also to point out that man can by understanding the natural process and by serendipity "plan" his individual and, to some extent, his collective course. Permission to quote from Mr. Hardin's book was given by the publishers: Holt, Rinehart & Winston, Inc., New York, and Jonathan Cape Ltd., London.

94. GEORGE H. MEAD: *Mind, Self and Society from the Standpoint of a Social Behaviorist*

Alfred North Whitehead has said of this work: "I report the publication of the volumes containing the late Professor George

Herbert Mead's researches as of the highest importance to philosophy. I entirely agree with Professor John Dewey's estimate, 'A seminal mind of the very first order.' "

Mead was a scientist of the first order, a social psychologist whose students thought so much of his lectures and notes that they have brought together his findings in this remarkable book, a unique book for this very reason. Mead's philosophy follows in the tradition of Aristotle, Descartes, Leibnitz, Russell, Whitehead, and Dewey—all of which points to the generalization that basically there is truly no sharp "separation or antagonism between the activities of science and philosophy," as these men themselves have so vividly demonstrated. As Mead put it: "The philosophy of a period is always an attempt to interpret its most secure knowledge."

Mead, the pragmatist, has given us a firm scientific base, philosophically sound, upon which to build a society more knowledgeable in handling its activities for its survival in the strategy of life. This is what the book is about. This society, so clearly pictured by Mead, is the highest level of integration that nature has produced. Man's brain (a primate brain), being the most complicated mechanism known to science, is the machinery through which the self operates, and in its operation mind appears. Where J. B. Watson held his psychology chiefly at the private level (that is, the individual level), Mead brilliantly demonstrated the weakness of this psychology and pushed the study to its logical conclusion, showing clearly that the self and mind are developed only in a social situation. It will be upon this platform, firmly secured by Mead's researches, that man will build an even more integrated and exciting society with all its unexpected emergents, truly strategic maneuvers which have been so successful in the past at all levels.

This book was edited with an introduction by Charles W. Morris, one of Mead's students, and published by the University of Chicago Press, Chicago (eleventh impression), 1957.

95. LANCELOT LAW WHYTE: *The Unitary Principle in Physics and Biology*

Whyte's book is based on a belief in the unity of nature. In the strategy of life there appears in many minds what Whyte calls an "arational feeling" that there might be a "hidden unity of form in nature, which the intellect had not yet identified." It is possible that this arational feeling is one of the "emergents" appearing in a "planless" world which will eventually aid in the "strategy of life," developing a unifying principle which will make a greater social cohesiveness, a necessary ingredient for survival. The book is an attempt to supply one of the first outlines of the unitary theory of organisms, which is all-encompassing from the single entity (organism) to the collective enterprise (social). This is provisional. In Whyte's words, ". . . it is not an essay in speculative philosophy or in merely terminological synthesis, since it is open to further development and to experimental test in relation to special problems."

The author concludes as follows:

> I regard this book as part of a co-operative and convergent movement in all the sciences, which is now at full flood. Apart from the unitary principle there is probably little new in it, and its dependence on much recent work, particularly in biology, is obvious. . . . But I cannot forbear to mention those who for me have thrown most light on the foundations of exact science: Bohr, Bridgeman, Broad, Curie, Eddington, Einstein, Heisenberg, Henderson (L. J.), Mach, Planck, Russell, and Whitehead. Nor those who have been my main teachers in biology: Adrian, Astbury, Child, Coghill, de Beer, Herrick, Huxley (J. S.), Jennings, Lashley, Lilly, Needham, Pauling, Seifritz, Waddington, Weiss and Woodger.

It is evident that we are in need of a new foundation in science which will establish a unity and a semblance of order.

The splintering of disciplines has exploded a mushroom of specialties which have long outrun synthesis. These accumulated specialties can only make sense by a discovery of a theoretical principle which is all-encompassing. This is what Whyte is pleading for. The need is equally great in physics, in biology, and psychology.

> Biology looks to physics but physical theory cannot give an adequate lead, for it is occupied in a basic reorganization and does not see its own way ahead. . . . Many biologists have suspected that the foundations of classical physics lack some element which is essential to biological theory for the value of every physical model has sooner or later been exhausted and the nature of biological organization still remains obscure. It is therefore possible that the crisis in physics is related to the crisis in biology and that both sciences must now move together on to a new common foundation.

Whyte's book, published in 1949 in New York by Henry Holt and Company, is exceedingly provocative. I know of no other which states the problem of unity so clearly. This "feeling" has been in the air now for some time. The neophyte should be familiar with this from the very beginning of his studies. Quotations used are by permission of the publisher and A. Watkins, Inc., agent for the author.

CHAPTER NINE

Appendix I
Why? *

It is a matter of record (Butterbrot und Schinken, *Geschichte der besch. Metaphysik,* xi, 296) that Socrates was accustomed to hand to each of his students a mimeographed *List of Required Reading,* along with the syllabus of the questions he proposed to ask at each session. And, to go back still further, is it not stated on authority which seems slightly dubious, I grant, but which may be sound, that the great Chinese emperor Fu-hi, who died in 2738 B.C., having invented matrimony, was reading on his death-bed a then just issued treatise entitled (I translate) *The Sixty-Nine Best Books,* now unfortunately lost?

And so it has gone down to our day. Sometimes the outpouring for the relief of this curiously contagious itch to tell other people what to read, which infects mankind, has been overtly labelled for what it is, as Lubbock's was and this little treatise is. In other cases the medicine has been skillfully flavored to disguise its real savor and purpose. Thus did Burton practice in his *Anatomy of Melancholy,* also the elder Disraeli in the *Curiosities of Literature,* and, to come nearer to the Victorian-Coolidgean epoch, so also Thomas Love Peacock and Anatole France. But if the thing has been so often done,

---

* Chapter 1 in Raymond Pearl, *To Begin With: Being Prophylaxis Against Pedantry* (New York and London: Alfred A. Knopf, 1927), pp. 1–13. Reproduced by permission of the publisher.

why do it again? Have the old medicines, still carefully preserved on our library shelves, no healing power left? And why should a mere biologist venture into so recondite a field?

The answer is simple and has already been implied. The whole thing is grounded in pathology. Such books as this are always engendered by a queer sort of illness, acute in respect of certain of its elements, but in others stubbornly chronic. In my own case the thing began with all the symptoms of influenza, and was so diagnosed and treated by the faculty. But the trouble was really of a far more insidious nature. While I was confined to the house congested respiratory tract within, and a multitude of books without, the virus which had probably long lurked in my system found its favorable moment, and pencil and paper had to be fetched forthwith to save my life. Here was the chance to do an article which would stop forever the annoyance of students always wanting to be told what they ought to read. At it I went, with mounting fever, and finished in two days the magazine article out of which this book later grew. On the third day I arose an apparently cured man.

So far I believe this to be an accurate description of a typical case of this strange disease. But it is not a complete picture of the syndrome. It neglects what is really its most important feature, the underlying psychopathic element. This takes the form of an hallucination that all is not well with the world. In particular, the poor harassed patient firmly believes that the young are going wrong and need sympathetic and wise guidance, before the harm to them, and correlatively to all humankind, is irremediable. The horrid vividness of this hallucination is beyond description. When the disease is at its height the delusion is fed by every newspaper, every social contact, and especially and particularly every student.

The disease was well known to the ancients. The Emperor Shi Hwang-ti, who began his reign in 246 B.C., not only had it in its most virulent form, but devised and carried out the most drastic and effective measures for its treatment ever known. His *therapeusis* has never been improved. While the acute illness twisted his viscera he personally examined, one by one, all the books which existed in China, at the rate of 120 pounds by weight *per diem;* set aside on the book shelves of the palace those which seemed to him worth reading and burned all the rest. There is every reason to suppose that he would have been completely and permanently cured by this course of treatment, but for one unfortunate fact. A group of professors, presumably fearful of losing their jobs if Shi's purge was allowed to finish itself, formed an association to defeat his purpose by secretly holding out books he had ordered burned. Some 460 of them were caught in this nefarious and inhuman business, and put to death. So putrid were their juices that melons actually grew in winter on the spot beneath which their bodies lay buried (Giles, *Chinese Biog. Dict.* 653). A number of others were banished for life. But some few super-smart assistant professors succeeded in concealing enough books, by bricking them up in walls and in other ways, so that poor Shi Hwang-ti's cure was never complete.

Turning now to the Western world, and about two centuries later, Quintus Horatius Flaccus, whose mental health otherwise was as cheerfully sound as could be desired, unquestionably had our disease in a mild but chronic form. Did he not point out (*Epist. I. ii.* 27–30) that while our strenuous idleness appears to drive us to seek the art of enjoying life by dashing about in automobiles, airplanes and express trains, this boon is really to be found in "the regulation of the mind, and not in the whisking about of the body."

In the most virulent form of the disease the hallucinations always center about the defects of the present system of educating our youth. The victim sees, with the most extraordinary clarity, its debasing and even ruinous tendencies. At the same time there suffuses through his whole being a great glow of mingled belief and hope that something effective could be done about it. Thus the Rev. Dr. Opimian, obviously suffering from a fearful attack, says (*Gryll Grange,* xix): "If all the nonsense which, in the last quarter of a century, has been talked on all other subjects were thrown into one scale, and all that has been talked on the subject of education alone were thrown into the other, I think the latter would preponderate." And again in the course of the same conversation: "Questions which can only be answered by the parrotings of a memory crammed to disease with all sorts of heterogeneous diet can form no test of genius, taste, judgment, or normal capacity. Competitive Examinations takes for its *norma:* 'It is better to learn many things ill than one thing well'; or rather: 'It is better to learn to gabble about everything than to understand anything.' This is not the way to discover the wood of which Mercuries are made. I have been told that this precious scheme has been borrowed from China; a pretty fountain-head for moral and political improvement: and if so, I may say, after Petronius: 'This windy and monstrous loquacity has lately found its way to us from Asia, and like a pestilential star has blighted the minds of youth otherwise rising to greatness.'"

Just as there is apparently no time limit to be set for the origin of this strange malady, in however remote antiquity, so there is no geographical bound to its pestilential spread. Lately a member of the National Academy of Sciences of our own prosperous commonwealth, has made a study of the elections to that occasionally immortal, though self-perpetuating, group of professors, and has published the results in their *Proceedings* (xi, 757–760). He found that during the 61 years of the Academy's history it had elected but 43 persons—almost exactly 10 percent of the total number ever elected—at an age under 37 years at the time of election. The remoteness of such an age from anything that can possibly be regarded as extreme youth indicates that the Academy has always been sceptical about any rapid flowering of genius. But even allowing for this wholly natural reluctance of the already immortal to recognize similar qualities in the still mortal, which was as characteristic of the denizens of Mt. Olympus (*cf.* Lucian, *Deorum concilium*) as it is of those of Mt. Wilson, this is not the whole story. Our investigator found that of these 43 men who succeeded in grasping the Grail before age 37, only 11 have accomplished it in the 40 years which have elapsed since 1884. This leads him to make the following remarks (*loc. cit.* 760): "It is easy to attribute the changing habits of the Academy relative to the election of young men to a growing conservatism of that body itself. That this is the sole cause I doubt. It is at least possible, and I incline personally to think it probable, that the increasing organization, standardization, mechanization and constant striving for efficient mediocrity in all our university and college life, which every thoughtful person has seen going on during the past 30 years, and which some have deplored and vainly endeavored to stop, is showing as one of its most dreadful effects the curbing and fettering of the progress of the really brilliant student. That some such idea as this is forcing itself upon many minds is indicated by the National Research Council's study of the problem of the brilliant student, under the direction of Professor C. E. Seashore and by Professor Wheeler's brilliant paper on 'The Dry-Rot of Our Academic Biology,' . . . [See selection No. 29]. Much ink has been spilled about the subject of academic freedom, but nearly always with reference to the freedom of the professors to do various things, sometimes obviously absurd or ridiculous. Is it not about time to consider seriously the subject of the freedom, within academic precincts, of the student to develop his intellectual powers in the way he personally wants to? Perhaps some slight concessions in this direction would in time have as one result, among many other desirable ones, some lowering of the average age of election to the National Academy of Sciences."

Not only is the temporal and geographical incidence of our disease extraordinarily widespread, as we have seen, but it attacks persons of the most varied occupations. Anyone who knows anything about the forwardness and upwardness of the outlook of university deans, would naturally suppose them to enjoy a complete immunity from this loathsome infection. But under date line of Paris, September 2, 1926, we find the eminent Dr. Ferdinand Brunot, dean of the faculty of letters of the University of Paris, quoted in the *Baltimore Evening Sun* to the following effect:

"The student coming from the *lycée* is about half-way," said the dean in commenting upon the throng of candidates from girls' schools seeking to enter the university. "She is evolving. How can we judge her? In the first place, there are too many of these students. And most of them are on the wrong road. A girl prepares her baccalaureate in Latin while she would do better in agriculture. The reason is bourgeois vanity. Parents from vanity want their children to gain an advanced education. They must be able, they believe, to answer affirmatively the question so often put today: 'Have you got your baccalaureate?' We have lost the fundamental family education that used to be so valuable. Forty years ago the young man who spoke slang was rebuked in his home. But now the son of a dairyman or a concierge, who may make good grades in the *lycée* or the college, often uses when at home a language representing the worst taste and nobody corrects him. We can readily observe the effects of this in the examinations—so many papers smack of the back-shop. In these papers on my desk are lines that are ridiculous. If they were published, they would be taken for the inventions of a humorist. In a single page of Latin we commonly find a dozen examples of bad spelling. We don't write French any longer because we don't speak it. That's the whole difficulty. The language established by the writers of the seventeenth century was that of the salons. Few writers knew French, but they wrote as they spoke, and their style was the purest and most measured in the world. We should not forget how our dictionary was made in 1694. The program of college instruction is badly chosen today. Students want above all to learn Latin, but if the student is talented it matters little what program he follows. We had an example this year when, in the general competition, the student who won the prize for dissertation did not know Latin. If parents were wiser, we could expect a great deal from their children."

These extracts from case histories must suffice for the exposition of the etiology and symptomatology of our malady. It remains to discuss briefly its treatment. Here unfortunately the results are disappointing, and lag far behind the progress which has been made in its diagnosis. The most that the faculty has been able to accomplish by any treatment is the alleviation, sometimes permanent but more often only temporary, of the acute symptoms. Nothing has been found to produce any effect whatever upon the chronic element of the disease except Shi Hwang-ti's treatment, which violates the code of medical ethics and therefore cannot be used. Fortunately, like the gout, to which incidentally our disease has many other points of resemblance, it is almost never fatal. The patient is pestered, but not pinnated.

For the acute symptoms the treatment of choice, indeed the only effective one available, is to provide the victim with writing materials and let nature take its course, depending upon the *vis medicatrix scribendi*. The dosage should be sufficient. A magazine article is not enough. It will produce a slight remission of the symptoms, but the effect is never more than temporary. A book is almost always necessary in the end, and may as well be exhibited at once.

What follows then, in this book, is my medicine. I can think of no better apology for letting it go forth than the good-humored, if perhaps ironical, words of Georges Duhamel in one of his *Lettres au Patagon:*

"*Toutes choses sont à leur place dans ce monde misérable, même le pathétique désir d'un monde meilleur.*"

CHAPTER TEN

Appendix II
*Wherefore**

In theory, at least, that special kind of intellectual activity which we call graduate study and in so doing emphasize the least important of its milestones, should give its practitioner a comprehensive, justly balanced, and critically related knowledge of the particular field whose charms have seduced him. Perhaps I ought more precisely to say that this was the theory in my youth, and is still clung to by some. But the prevalence and power of this view are unmistakably diminishing. This is perhaps chiefly because of the closer and closer integration of the advanced and graduate activities in our universities with the rest of the highly formalized and mechanized system of education which prevails in the land and is in such perfect accord with the cultivation of that efficient, standardized mediocrity which seems to be the very spirit and genius of American civilization. It is now quite possible, in fact it probably has been done, for a boy to go straight through from his letter blocks to his Ph.D. with precisely the same kind of cooperation in the enterprise on his part that a sardine furnishes to the business of his translation from the state of innocence and freedom of his birthplace to the diploma-bearing tin on the grocer's shelf. All that is requisite is a certain self-effacing con-

* Chapter 2 in Pearl, Raymond, *To Begin With: Being Prophylaxis Against Pedantry* (New York and London: Alfred A. Knopf, 1927), pp. 13-23. Reproduced by permission of the publisher.

87

formity to a series of propulsive mechanisms. Perhaps this is as it should be. Certainly he is a bold, if not indeed a rash, person who attempts to stand athwart the current of his civilization. But without being so extreme in the matter as this would imply, the idea still somewhat widely prevails that, without interfering in any important way with the smoothness of the established methods of manufacturing doctors of philosophy, and without curtailing the output of this commodity, it is desirable, and should be possible, to make the graduate student take a more active personal interest in the process of his transfiguration than the sardine may be presumed to. During the quarter of a century that I have tried to function as an insignificant cog in certain of the mechanisms referred to, the problem of how best to make those machines more useful has intermittently but still extensively engaged my attention. The instinct of workmanship is fairly deep-seated. We all like to do as good a job as we can. It has fallen out that my duties have been mainly to aid in the progress of graduate students along their appointed chutes. The problem has been: How may that basic ideal of graduate instruction stated in the first sentence of this chapter best be promoted? Not solely by lectures, it is generally agreed. There are two fundamental objections to this method; the first that it would make insufferable inroads on the professors' diversions, the other that it tends to perpetuate the intellectual inertia begotten in the student's undergraduate course.

The only other way yet heard of to accomplish the end sought is that known as directed reading. The instructor is supposed to outline a course of reading for the student which will make him privy to at least the major secrets of his subjects. The advantages of this method are obvious. The student does something for himself. At its best he gets the sense of professional craft solidarity. He becomes really initiated into the realm of scholarship and makes contact with the great minds that have built the structure whose architecture he must know before he can add his bit to it. At the worst he has satisfied a requirement of the manufacturing process with a minimum amount of trouble to his instructor.

But granting the fundamental soundness of the pedagogical device of directed reading for graduate students, there still remains the problem for the instructor of determining on a general principle for the guiding of this reading. Obviously the student can not read in the three years of his graduate study as much of his subject as the instructor has in the, let us say, *n* years of his professional life. A selection must be made from the treasures at command. But upon what principle shall this selection be made? It is this question which has vexed my mind, and I fancy that of many another in similar position. What I used to do was to make out lists of highly technical researches in the particular field of interest and tell the student that along that pathway was the road to salvation. This I am sure was a mistake. It started from a false assumption. The progression was forthwith to the special on the supposition that the general has been taken care of. But nothing could be more ridiculous nonsense than such an assumption. In consequence of the widely prevailing pedagogical theory that needlework, jigsawing, salesmanship and many other kindred academic disciplines are of at least equal cultural and intellectual value in the training of our youth to the study of Greek or Latin or mathematics or chemistry; coupled with the permission, if not active encouragement to the undergraduate to specialize during his mental infancy, it results that when the young things begin serious graduate work a solidly grounded general background upon which to build a sound specialism is precisely what, generally speaking, they most completely lack.

What then to do? Plainly the obligation is to repair as much as may be of the damage that has been wrought from omission and commission, by putting in the way of the student the means of orienting himself relative to his subject on the one hand and to the general *corpus* of human learning on the other hand. If he amounts to anything he will then guide himself to the technical reading in his chosen subject better than any one else can steer him. If, by chance, he is not one of God's anointed, no harm will have been done. He will at least have glimpsed some little part of the evidence that

> Man's mind a mirror is of heavenly sights,
> A brief wherein all marvels summèd lie,

and in all probability will ever after lead a better life, even though he fails to become much of a biologist or statistician.

After thought, and the application of the method of trial and error, I evolved the course of reading for my graduate students which it is the purpose of this book to exhibit. At the outstart it should be explained that the university students for whom this list was primarily designed are looking forward, for the most part, to careers connected in some manner near or remote with pure biology or with public health. Mainly they want to become qualified biologists or vital statisticians or biometricians. Some regard academic halls as the optimum environment for their souls' ultimate expansion; others look forward to a career of usefulness in an official bureau or an independent research institution. All intend, bless their innocent hearts, to become investigators, researchers, small or great as *Allah* may will, but anyhow members in good standing of the holy brotherhood of those curious to know. All these considerations have played their due part in the making of the list. But what has been of the greatest importance in determining its final constitution is that public health, vital statistics and biometry are all, when properly viewed, parts or branches of *biology*. Naturally, if one were making such a list for an embryo physicist or chemist some of the items on the present would be replaced with others more directly pertinent to those lines of endeavor. But not all would be so re-placed. A certain philosophical generality which taints and savors the list as a whole is perhaps its most engaging feature.

Let not the budding biologist suppose that he may with impunity omit the chapter devoted to statistical works, nor the embryo statistician think that he will lose nothing by skipping that which lists the strictly biological books. Virtu-ally all biologists would be a great deal better off intellectually if they knew more than they do of the fundamentals of sta-tistics. And a vital statistician who has not been steeped in the essential juices of biology is simply mis-labelled. He may be a statistician, but he is not likely to be particularly vital.

The list of books set forth in the remaining chapters of this little treatise is divided into four main parts on the following philosophy. Any person who intends to make his living and to spend his life at science plainly ought first of all to have the clearest possible understanding as to what science is and what it is all about, in a broad philosophical and *human* sense. This means that he should have some notion of the main events in the history of human thought. Such an understanding should come early in the course of professional scientific study. Per-haps the student is embarking on a scientific career under a misapprehension as to what science really is. Such cases have been known. They are always sad and may be tragic. Hence Chapter III, "Underpinning."

Because a person, from however pure and noble motives, elects to be a worker in science he is not thereby absolved from the duties and privileges of being human. He must work out an adjustment between the claims upon his life of his science, a proverbially jealous and exacting mistress, and those of the rest of the world, including not only deans, committees, com-missioners, directors, boards, foundations and other great cos-mic elements, but also cooks, maids, nurses, children, and most important of all, his wife. While no one else can make these adjustments for him, still it will help to know how others have met the problem. Again if our graduate student, in whose behalf we are taking all this trouble, turns out to amount to much he will sooner or later receive offers for the purchase of his soul. Such offers will be made by those skilled in the traffic and they will be tempting. A little knowledge of the technique in these matters will not be amiss. Shall we not be derelict in our job of helping our student to get his training for life if we do not furnish him some insight into what wisdom is available about the making of these necessary adjustments between scientific research and the rest of life? I think so. Hence Chapter IV, "Living."

Since the central element of the whole enterprise is biological the presence of Chapter V, "Biology," needs no special argument.

Finally, and obviously, my student may be intending to earn his living by the practice of a particular scientific trade. Hence Chapter VI, "Biostatistics." I attach great importance to the order of the several items in the list. The maximum effect will be produced by reading them in precisely the sequence in which they are set down, I believe.

So far in this chapter I have followed closely the magazine article, which was originally really intended only for my own university students. But, as has already been explained, that little paper attracted wider attention than had been expected or intended. It appeared that the general reader was interested in the list. Upon reflection this seemed reasonable. The "general reader," in so far as he reads more than the sub-titles of moving pictures, or that noble mirror of American civilization founded by Benjamin Franklin and theoretically published on Saturdays, is in fact a "graduate student." He has graduated from something. To be a student one does not have to be registered in a university.

So in revising and extending the original list I have kept this larger group in mind. And to safeguard this generalized graduate student I have marked with an asterisk those items in the list which can be guaranteed not to bite him. My meaning is that the starred titles in the first place presume no technical training in any particular science or philosophy, and in the second place are, on the whole, both easy and entertaining to read. [Reader must see more of Pearl's book to use this information.]

CHAPTER ELEVEN

Epilogue

This list lacks much that should be said concerning religious matters. It also has no references to food, drink, music, and the graphic arts, all of which are closely interwoven with living. To compensate for this, the following works are suggested:

This Believing World, by Lewis Browne, published by Macmillan, in New York, 1926.

Man and His Gods, by Homer W. Smith, an outstanding physiologist, whose specialty was the kidney but who had a profound insight into the natural history of man, especially man's early animistic tendencies. Albert Einstein, in the foreword to the book says, "This is a biologist speaking, whose scientific training has disciplined him in a grim objectivity rarely found in the pure historian." The book was issued in Boston, in 1953, by Little, Brown & Company.

The Varieties of Religious Experience: A Study in Human Nature, by William James. James advocated a tough-minded attitude in all things human. The book was first published in 1902, and went through 35 reprintings by 1928. These were all by Longman's, Green & Co., of New York. A paperback by the New American Library of New York was printed in 1961.

Science Ponders Religion, edited by Harlow Shapley, is a collection of essays by eighteen leading American scientists. It was published by Appleton-Century-Crofts, Inc., of New York, in 1960.

Is It God's World?, by Joseph Wheless, published in New York by Alfred A. Knopf, Inc., 1926. There is also a two-volume paperback edition by the Dover Press.

A History of the Warfare of Science with Theology in Christendom, by Andrew Dickson White, 2 volumes, published in New York by D. Appleton & Co., 1923.

These books, along with Herrick's *Evolution of Human Nature,* Teilhard de Chardin's *The Phenomenon of Man,* and Dixon's *The Human Situation,* should bring some satisfaction to one's religious longings as well as to prepare one for serious thinking about man's nature.

Professor J. C. Eccles in *The Neurophysiological Basis of Mind* (Oxford at the Clarendon Press, 1953) asks the question, "Who Are We?" The books on religion just previously mentioned help answer this question.

About food: Pearl lists only one book, Brillat-Savarin's *La Physiologie du Goût,* remarking that "the truly great book on gastronomy is yet to be written." Pearl further states that Brillat-Savarin has a great deal that is "cheap" and contains much "wholly irrelevant philosophy." Pearl suggests that the best treatise on food is Curronsky and Marcel Rouff's 20-volume *La France Gastronomique. Guide des merveilles et des bonnes auberges françaises* (Paris: Rouff). As the reader can see, it deals only with French food. I think the French have given to the Western world its best cuisine.

Concerning drink: Pearl had a great deal to say about H. Warner Allen's *The Wines of France,* published in London by T. Fisher Unwin, in 1924. This delightful and sophisticated book should be read by all, for nothing is more pleasing than good wine, and one should know of what he drinks!

A new era of art appreciation has dawned on the scene of American higher education. Most students now know something about good music and graphic arts. Man, even with limited ability, can actively participate in these two forms of art. Reasonably priced reproductions of the great masterpieces of paintings and etchings are available. These have to be experienced and not just read about.

Index